MATHS FOR THE MORE
YEAR 4

Rising Stars UK Ltd, part of Hodder Education, an Hachette UK Company,
Carmelite House, 50 Victoria Embankment, London, EC4Y 0DZ
www.risingstars-uk.com

Published 2013
Reprinted 2014 (twice), 2015 (twice), 2016

Author: Steph King
Creation of characters, context/storyline and additional material: Richard Cooper
Education Consultant: Cherri Moseley
Typesetting: Words & Pictures Ltd
Cover design: Burville-Riley Partnership
Publisher: Kate Jamieson
Project manager: Bruce Nicholson Publishing
Artwork: Barking Dog Art, Words & Pictures Ltd

British Library Cataloguing in Publication Data.
A CIP record for this book is available from the British Library.

ISBN: 978-1-78339-073-1

INTRODUCTION

The Story So Far ...

The Mariners struggled to settle on Mars – they had to overcome problems such as homesickness, fierce solar radiation and growing their own food. However, they were able to explore more of their new home in the Martian Rover and also discovered a precious metal which they have called '*Gagarin-Gold*'.

We're finally beginning to settle into our Martian lives.

JADE

Maths for the More Able

This exciting new series gives your students the opportunity to engage in contextualised mathematics that extends the programme of studies for the new National Curriculum. Its aim is for children to deepen their understanding of the mathematics involved through application and opportunities to reason at a higher level.

Each unit contains two pages of student activities, accompanied by one page of notes for the teacher, which provide an overview of the content. They also include prompts to help the teacher consider whether the children have the required skills and knowledge that will need to be applied to the problems (Key knowledge). Additionally, teachers are provided with prompts for assessing and evaluating the children's strategies along with ideas to further extend a problem. There is also a comprehensive set of solutions for the questions in the unit.

he student activities are broken into four sections, 'Starting Off', 'Away We Go!', 'Free Running' and
I.D.'s Challenge', which are structured so that the problems become increasingly more demanding as
e unit progresses. Units can be used flexibly so that, should an activity prove too challenging at one
int, with a quick recap, it can be revisited later in the year when the children are ready to tackle the
ext stage in the challenge.

athematical reasoning is an integral part of this resource and children will be expected to explain
eir thinking as part of their solutions. On occasions, this will be accompanied by a language structure
guide explanations, e.g. 'I think Dara is right because ...'

part of the challenges, children will find hints as reminders, additional information or suggestions
out how best to present their findings. However, generally they will be expected to show their
dings in their own way.

ith a strong focus on problem solving, there will be times when the use of a calculator should be
couraged so that the children have the freedom to explore more thoroughly and change their
ategies more easily when an incorrect path has been followed.

e hope you and your students enjoy their Mission to Mars!

elp Dara, Zack, Ceri and Jade and the team overcome the new challenges that arise on Mars by
lving the maths problems.

DARA

CERI

ZACK

JADE

CONTENTS

Destination - Olympus Mons   5

On Top of Olympus Mons   8

Inter-Planetary Heroes!   11

News About *Gagarin-Gold* Gets Out ...   14

The Rover Breaks Down   17

Back to Base   20

Water on Mars?   23

Strange Tracks in the Soil   26

A Close Encounter with the *Curiosity* Rover   29

Life On Mars?   32

An Amazing Discovery   35

Follow the Leader   38

A Rift Opens Up   41

Two Sides to Everything   44

The Mission in Crisis   47

Making Up   50

An M-POD Makeover   53

Repairing the Rover   56

Working with *Curiosity*   59

A Brief Encounter ...   62

DESTINATION – OLYMPUS MONS

Solving problems about decimals.

➤ An expedition to Olympus – the highest mountain and largest volcano in the Solar System. It is almost three times the height of Mount Everest.

△ Starting Off

Attention, Mariners! Today you must start your expedition to Olympic Mons. We are keen to explore this mountain and volcano as scientists on Earth want more photographic evidence of its magnitude.

The special lenses make objects appear much closer. The 10× zoom lens makes objects appear 10 times closer. This means than an object 20 metres away would look like it was only 2 metres away!

We'll need to take the camera equipment and the special lenses to get some good shots!

1. Copy and complete the table to show how the different lenses work.

	20 metres	42 metres	? metres	258 metres	? metres
10× zoom	2 metres				
100× zoom			1.75 metres		
1000× zoom					0.5 metres

◁ Away We Go

Let's write some of these measurements down so we can put this information with the images. We will need to show the value of each digit in the number too.

100× zoom

345 m	3.45 m
73 m	?
105 m	?
99.9 m	?

Jade writes down the new measurements like this using partitioning to help her:

$$3.45 \text{ m} = 3 \text{ m} + \frac{4}{10} \text{ m} + \frac{5}{100} \text{ m}$$

1. Find the new measurements with the 100× zoom and show the value of each digit in the same way that Jade has done here.

2. Round each of the new measurements to the nearest whole metre (e.g. 3.45 m would round down to 3 m).

| 2 .34 m | 2.43 m | 3.24 m | 2.04 m | 2.3 m |

Jade writes down these five measurements.

3. Help Jade write all of these measurements in order, from smallest to largest. Find a way to prove your decision each time.

HINT: You could use partitioning to help you prove your decisions.

4. Write down another **two** measurements that would go between the ones shown here. One of the numbers should have **only tenths** and the other should have **tenths and hundredths**.

| | | | ↓ | | |

smallest   largest

▷ Free Running

The Mariners are in the Rover and on the way to Olympus Mons.
Dara is driving, so Jade, Ceri and Zack have been busy taking many digital images along the way.

Each Mariner is using a different lens on their camera.

| 10× zoom | 100× zoom | 1000× zoom |

1. Use the clues below to find out which Mariner has taken which images and what lens they are using.

- The Mariner was standing 2850 m away when they took the image of Olympus Mons.
- Jade used the lens that made the strange rock look 3.05 m away when it was really 305 m away!
- The image of Mount Sharp makes it look only 125.4 m away.
- Ceri took the image of the mountain that appeared to be about 3 m away.

S.I.D.'s Challenge

Use what you have found out to complete this table.

	Lens used	Actual distance	Distance in image, e.g. 3.41 m	Rounded to one decimal place, e.g. 3.41 m rounds to 3.4 m
Olympus Mons	× ?			
Strange rock	× ?			
Mount Sharp	× ?			

6

DESTINATION – OLYMPUS MONS

TEACHER'S NOTES

Curriculum Focus

. Find the effect of dividing a one- or two-digit number by 10, 100 (and 1000), identifying the value of the digits in the answer as units, tenths and hundredths.
. Round decimals with one decimal place to the nearest whole number (and with two decimal places to the nearest number with one decimal place).
. Compare numbers with the same number of decimal places up to two decimal places.

Running the Activity

Background

How secure are the children using a place value grid to multiply and divide numbers by 10, 100 (and 1000)? How confidently can they explain the effect on the digits and the use of zero as a place holder?

What experience do they have of working with measure and applying knowledge of place value to make sense of the value of each digit, particularly for decimals? Can they explain the rules for rounding?

Can they confidently partition numbers with one or two decimal places using this notation? $U + \dfrac{?}{10} + \dfrac{?}{100}$

These tasks require children to multiply and divide numbers by 10, 100 and 1000 in a problem-solving context and be able to round to the nearest whole number and to one decimal place.

Starting Off

Within *Starting Off*, children use the given criteria to divide values by 10, 100 and 1000. They are also required to use the inverse.

Key knowledge: When dividing by 10, 100 and 1000, the digits move to the right by one, two or three places, respectively. Zeros are needed as place holders so that we know that the number is now 10, 100 or 1000 times smaller.

Away We Go

Within *Away We Go*, children move on to partitioning decimal numbers to include tenths, hundredths and thousandths. The problem extends to ordering decimals including comparing one and two decimal places.

Key knowledge: To compare one and two decimal place numbers, it is useful to consider tenths expressed in hundredths, i.e. 2.3 as 2.30 to help compare it with 2.34.

Free Running

Within *Free Running*, children are presented with a logic problem involving the skills used so far.

In *S.I.D.'s Challenge* they must also apply skills of rounding to one decimal place.

Sharing Results and Evaluating

Look for children who make use of the place value grid to help them make sense of dividing by 10, 100 and 1000. Look for children who confidently explain the use of the zero as a place holder.
Share examples of rounding and ask children to suggest other decimal numbers that can be rounded to the same amount.

Answers

Starting Off

1.

	20 metres	42 metres	175 metres	258 metres	500 metres
10× and	2 metres	4.2 m	17.5 m	25.8 m	50 m
100× zoom	0.2 m	0.42 m	1.75 m	2.58 m	5 m
1000× zoom	0.02 m	0.042 m	0.175 m	0.258 m	0.5 m

Away We Go

1. 73 $\longrightarrow$ 0.73 $0.73 = 0 + \dfrac{7}{10} + \dfrac{3}{100}$

   105 $\longrightarrow$ 1.05 $1.05 = 1 + \dfrac{5}{100}$

   99.9 $\longrightarrow$ 0.999 $0.999 = 0 + \dfrac{9}{10} + \dfrac{9}{100} + \dfrac{9}{1000}$

2. 0.73 m, 1.05 m and 0.999 m all round to 1 m.
3. 2.04 m, 2.3 m, 2.34 m, 2.43 m, 3.43 m
4. 2.4 (one decimal place) is the only value that can go between 2.34 m and 2.43 m. There are more solutions for a value with two decimal place, e.g. 2.35 m, 2.36 m, 2.37 m (2.40 m!), 2.41 m and 2.42 m.

Free Running

Jade 100× zoom strange rock
Ceri 1000× zoom Olympus Mons
Zack 10× zoom Mount Sharp

S.I.D.'s Challenge

	Lens used	Actual distance	Distance in image, e.g. 3.41 m	Rounded to one decimal place, e.g. 3.41 m rounds 3.4 m
Olympus Mons	×1000	2850 m	2.85 m	2.9 m
Strange rock	×100	305 m	3.05 m	3.1 m
Mount Sharp	×10	1254 m	125.4 m	125.4 m

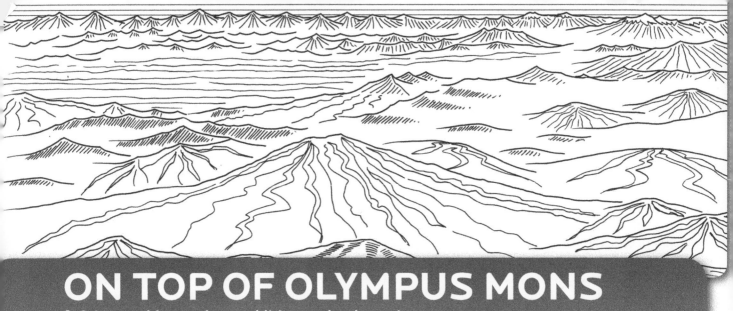

ON TOP OF OLYMPUS MONS
Solving problems about addition and subtraction.

➤ After a tiring climb, the Mariners reach a perfect viewing point from the top of Olympus Mons, the highest mountain and largest volcano in the solar system.

 Starting Off

The Mariners use their Mars e-device to help them get a better idea of the average height of some of the other mountains here on Mars.

> Wow, we can see for miles from here. Everything looks so far away and so small …

Dara remembers that S.I.D. reported a recent dust storm was so violent that nothing could be seen for the first 2000 m above the surface of Mars.
This made the mountains look much, much lower …

1. How high would each of the mountain have appeared in this violent dust storm?
   Write the calculation you used each time.

2. Dara calculated that only 1856 m of Euripus Mons could be seen. Jade knew he had made a mistake without even calculating. How did she know? *'Jade knows because …'*

3. What does your answer to question 1 tell you about Labeatis Mons during the dust storm?

Mars Data Mountains	
Mount Sharp	5500 m
Arsia Mons	17779 m
Pavonis Mons	14037 m
Alba Mons	6815 m
Euripus Mons	3945 m
Labeatis Mons	1143 m

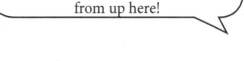 Away We Go

> The heights of the mountains are very different. We should compare some of the heights. It's quite difficult to tell from up here!

1. Choose at least **three** pairs of mountains and compare their heights. Show the three calculations you used.

2. Zack compared two mountains. He used the following calculation to check his working.

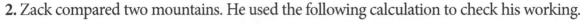

$$6815 \text{ m} + \underline{7222}\text{m} = 14{,}037 \text{ m}$$

Which two mountains did he compare and what is the missing value in his calculation?

There are lots of 'fiddly' numbers here to think about. Can't we just round them to give us an estimated height?

HINT: Remember to use the rules of rounding to help you.

The Mariners think this is a great idea and round the height of each mountain to the nearest 100 m.

3. Why do you think they are not rounding to the nearest 1000 m?
  'I think … because …'

4. Help the Mariners round each of the heights to the nearest 100 m.

Free Running

The Mariners decide to compare the mountains again using the heights that have been rounded to the nearest 100 m.

Explore how these compare with the exact calculations you made earlier. Find a way to show by how much the answers differ each time.

HINT: You may find it useful to show your findings in a table. Think carefully about the headings you will use to explain what each part of your table shows.

S.I.D.'s Challenge

The numbers in the shaded shapes are the differences between the two numbers on either side connected by the lines.

All the missing values are four-digit multiples of one hundred. None of these are the same.

Find a solution to the puzzle. **Don't forget the shapes on the diagonal lines!**

Can you find more than one solution?

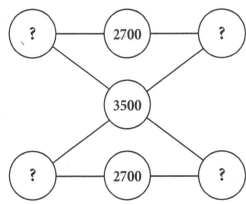

9

ON TOP OF OLYMPUS MONS

TEACHER'S NOTES

Curriculum Focus

1. Find 1000 more or less than a given number round any number to the nearest 10, 100 or 1000.
2. Estimate and use inverse operations to check answers to a calculation.
3. Solve number problems that involve increasingly large positive numbers.

Running the Activity

Background

Are the children confident when adding and subtracting multiples of 10, 100 and 1000? Can they explain how the number will change each time and what will stay the same?

What experience do they have of applying the rules of rounding to the nearest 100 to much larger numbers? Can they explain the rules and explain how this works for rounding to the nearest 1000?

These tasks also require children to find the difference between four- and five-digit numbers and between larger multiples of 100.

Starting Off

Within *Starting Off*, children are to subtract 2000 m from the given heights. They should use knowledge of place value rather than applying a written method.

> *Key knowledge:* When adding and subtracting multiples of one thousand, the value of the hundreds, tens and units and will always stay the same unless zero is crossed.

Away We Go

Within *Away We Go*, children move on to finding the difference between heights shown in metres. They should apply appropriate methods to calculate and then consider the inverse for checking. The problem develops to consider rounding to the nearest 100.

> *Key knowledge:* When rounding to the nearest 100, look for the TU values that are 50 or more and round these up to the next 100. Round down for TU values less than 50.

Free Running

Within *Free Running*, children are comparing rounded values to actual values and considering the difference between these two results.

In *S.I.D.'s Challenge* a puzzle involving the difference between multiples of one hundred is to be solved.

Sharing Results and Evaluating

Look for children who use inappropriate methods to subtract 2000 rather than using knowledge of place value.
Look for the range of methods children use to compare mountain heights. Do they appropriately choose when to find the difference and when to subtract the lower value from the higher?
Share possible solutions for *S.I.D.'s Challenge*.

Answers
Starting Off

1. Mount Sharp 5500 m − 2000 m = 3500 m
   Arsia Mons 17779 m − 2000 m = 15779 m
   Pavonis Mons 14037 m − 2000 m = 12037 m
   Alba Mons 6815 m − 2000 m = 4815 m
   Euripus Mons 3945 m − 2000 m = 1945 m
   Labeatis Mons 1143 m − 2000 m = ___
2. Jade knows because when a multiple of one thousand is added or subtracted, the value of the hundreds, tens and units will always stay the same.
3. It could not be seen at all!

Away We Go

1. Children's own comparisons, e.g. 5500 m − 3945 m = 1555 m (Mount Sharp and Euripus Mons) 17779 m − 14037 m = 3742 m (Arsia Mons and Pavonis Mons)
2. Alba Mons and Pavonis Mons 6815 + 7222 = 14037 m
3. 'I think they are not rounding to the nearest 1000 m because it would make the measurements less accurate.'
4. Mount Sharp (5500 m); Arsia Mons (17,800 m); Pavonis Mons (14,000 m); Alba Mons (6800 m); Euripus Mons (3900 m); Labeatis Mons (1100 m)

Free Running
Example table would include:

Mountain heights compared		Difference between rounded values (to nearest 100 m)	Actual difference measured	Difference (rounded and actual)
Mount Sharp 5500 m	Euripus Mons 3900 m	1600 m	1555 m	Actual is 45 m lower
Pavonis Mons 14000 m	Alba Mons 6800 m	7200 m	7222 m	Actual is 22 m higher
Euripus Mons 3900 m	Labeatis Mons 1100 m	2800 m	2802 m	Actual is 2 m higher

S.I.D.'s Challenge
Solutions include:
Top left 8700, top right 6000, bottom left 2500 and bottom right 5200
Top left 5000, top right 2300, bottom left 5800 and bottom right 8500

INTER-PLANETARY HEROES!

Solving problems about statistics.

➤ Since the mission first began, the world has been on the edge of its seat waiting to hear news of discoveries and, somehow, feel a little bit closer to life on the Red Planet!

△ Starting Off

This information appeared in the newspaper *Today is the Day*!

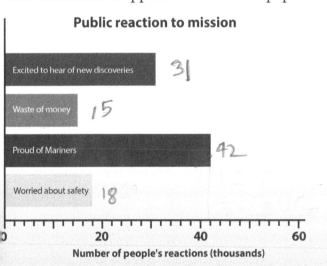

Public reaction to mission

Excited to hear of new discoveries	31
Waste of money	15
Proud of Mariners	42
Worried about safety	18

0   20   40   60

Number of people's reactions (thousands)

Mariners, here is more data from Earth about the public's reactions to our mission.

1. How many people think that the mission is a waste of money?

2. How many **more** people are proud of the Mariners than worried about safety?

3. Compare other public reactions in the same way and write a statement about each.

◁ Away We Go

S.I.D. showed the Mariners another table displaying the public reactions of a different group of people. This table was printed in *The Daily Spread* newspaper.

Public reaction	Number of people's reactions (thousands)
Excited to hear of new discoveries	ⅢⅢ ⅢⅢ ⅢⅢ ⅢⅢ ⅢⅢ Ⅲ
Waste of money	ⅢⅢ ⅢⅢ Ⅱ
Proud of Mariners	ⅢⅢ ⅢⅢ Ⅲ
Worried about safety	ⅢⅢ ⅢⅢ

1. How many thousands of people had each reaction in *The Daily Spread* newspaper?

2. What is the difference between the number of each of the public reactions in Today is the Day! and *The Daily Spread*?

11

But what is the total number of each reaction from **both** newspapers?

HINT: Remember to use a ruler and label your bar chart carefully.

3. Use the data from *Today is the Day*! and *The Daily Spread* to draw a new bar chart showing the **total** reactions.

Use the **same scale** as before.

4. How many people **in total** gave their reaction to the mission?

▷ Free Running

Hey, look! Here is the data to show how many people from the United Kingdom visited our Mission website in a day.

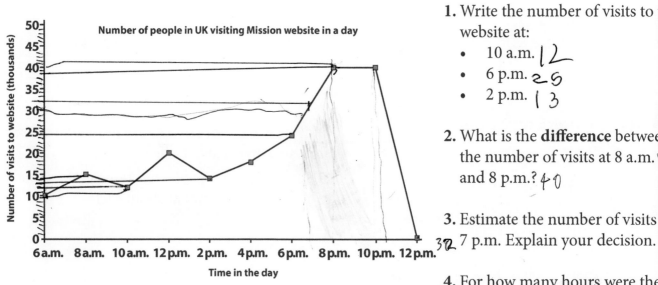

Number of people in UK visiting Mission website in a day

Number of visits to website (thousands)

Time in the day

1. Write the number of visits to t website at:
- 10 a.m. 12
- 6 p.m. 25
- 2 p.m. 13

2. What is the **difference** betwee the number of visits at 8 a.m. and 8 p.m.? 40

3. Estimate the number of visits 7 p.m. Explain your decision. 32

4. For how many hours were the **40,000** visits to the website?
2 hrs

S.I.D.'s Challenge

Why do you think the number of visits change so much across the day?

Think about the possible answer to Jade's question.

Use the information to tell the 'story' of t time graph. Your story **must** say somethin about the number of visits made at differe times in the day **and** give reasons for the changes during the day.

INTER-PLANETARY HEROES!

TEACHER'S NOTES

Curriculum Focus

. Interpret and present discrete data and continuous data using appropriate graphical methods, including bar charts and time graphs.
. Solve comparison, sum and difference problems using information presented in bar charts, pictograms, tables and other graphs.

Running the Activity

Background

Do the children regularly discuss and interpret data presented in different ways? How confident are they to make estimates about unknown values, particularly when the labels are less frequent along the scale?

Can they explain why a bar chart might be used and what type of data it could present? How confident are they reading data presented in a tally?

Do they understand the importance of reading a scale accurately and identifying the intervals used so that a range of values, including those on unlabelled increments, can be calculated?

These tasks require children to solve a range of problems using discrete data and a time graph. They must compare bar charts representing similar data.

Starting Off

Within *Starting Off*, children read values from a bar chart and make comparative statements about the data shown.

> **Key knowledge:** It is important to check the scale on a chart, graph or any other graphic representation of data so you can read it accurately.

Away We Go

Within *Away We Go*, children move on to reading a tally chart and making comparisons between two sets of similar data.

The problem extends to look at the total number of public reactions. Children are then required to draw and label their own bar chart.

> **Key knowledge:** Tally charts are set out in groups of five. It is easy to count in fives and quick to recognise (subitise) an amount less than 5.

Free Running

Within *Free Running*, children are using a time graph to help answer questions about the number of visits to the Mission website in a day.

In *S.I.D.'s Challenge* they must reason about the changes in numbers, i.e. the peak and low times and tell the 'story' of the graph.

Sharing Results and Evaluating

Look for children who use the knowledge of the number line to help identify values.
Share stories from *S.I.D.'s Challenge* and ask the children to evaluate the stories by following the time graph as the story is told.

Answers

Starting Off

1. 15,000
2. 24,000 (42,000 – 18,000)
3. 3000 more were worried about safety than it being a waste of money. 11,000 more were proud of the Mariners than were excited to hear news of discoveries, etc.

Away We Go

1. Excited 29,000, Waste of money 12,000, Proud 13,000 and Worried about safety 10,000
2. Differences: Excited 2000, Waste of money 3000, Proud 29,000 and Worried about safety 8000
3.

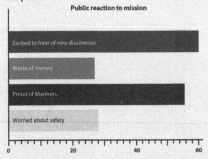

4. 170,000

Free Running

1. 12,000 (10 a.m.); 24,000 (6 p.m.); 14,000 (2 p.m.)
2. 25,000
3. 32,000 (midway point) accept 30,000 to 35,000
4. 2 hours (8-10 p.m.)

S.I.D.'s Challenge

Children's own story, e.g.
Only 10,000 people visited the website at 6 a.m. as it is very early in the morning and people are still asleep or getting ready for work/school, etc.
Other reasons (e.g. tea break, lunch break, coffee break/children home from school, evening so people at home, bedtime, asleep at midnight, etc.)

NEWS ABOUT *GAGARIN-GOLD* GETS OUT ...

Solving problems about money, time and statistics.

➤ After the Mariners' amazing discovery of *Gagarin-gold* earlier in the year, news has spread like wildfire an
its estimated value is rocketing!

◭ Starting Off

> Attention, Mariners. This is Earth Control.
> We wanted to update you about the news
> of your amazing discovery.
> Everyone wants to know about *Gagarin-gold*!

The Mariners print out a bar chart showing the number
of newspapers and magazines that have run a feature
on *Gagarin-gold* in the past five days.

Unfortunately the scale is missing, so the Mariners
are not sure what each bar represents.

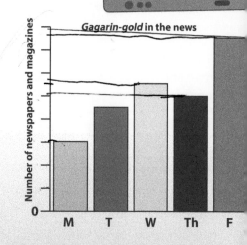

Gagarin-gold in the news

1. How many newspapers or magazines featured *Gagarin-gold*
   on **Monday** if the scale goes up in intervals (jumps) of:

   a 1500? **b** 1800? **c** 2500?
2. Write the value for **Tuesday** for each of the scales used
   above.

◁ Away We Go

> Mariners, I can just about make out
> that the value for **Thursday** is 8000.

> That's great S.I.D., now we can
> work out how many newspapers
> and magazines *Gagarin-gold*
> featured in each day.

1. What calculation will Zack use to find out the scale on the bar chart?
2. Using the scale, find the values for Monday, Tuesday, Wednesday and Friday.
3. On which two days was there a difference of exactly **4000** newspapers and magazines?

14

The Daily Spread and *Today is the Day!* ran features on *Gagarin-gold* everyday that week. The newspapers sold at record speed.

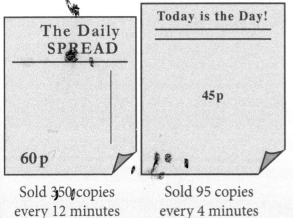

The Daily SPREAD

60 p

Sold 350 copies every 12 minutes

Today is the Day!

45 p

Sold 95 copies every 4 minutes

4. Calculate the number of copies each newspaper sold in **2 hours**. *30*

5. How much money was spent on each newspaper in **total** in two hours? Show your answer in pounds (£).

> **HINT:** Use what you know about the number of minutes in an hour to help you.

▷ Free Running

> Hey, guys, look what the newspapers are saying about the price of a gram (g) of *Gagarin-gold*, should more be found! It seems to be worth more by the hour!

Price (£)

Estimated price per gram (g) of *Gagarin-gold* in a day

80 –
72 –
64 –
56 –
48 –
40 –
32 –
24 –
16 –
8 –
0

8 a.m. 10 a.m. 12 p.m. 2 p.m. 4 p.m. 6 p.m. 8 p.m.

Time in the day

1. Use the time graph to find out how much one gram (g) of *Gagarin-gold* was estimated to be worth at each time of the day.

2. What is the value of **7 g** of *Gagarin-gold* at **4 p.m.**?

S.I.D.'s Challenge

Investigate to find out the estimate for the value of 7 g of *Gagarin-gold* at:

   9 a.m.   11 a.m.   3 p.m.   7 p.m.

How much do you think it could be worth at 9 p.m.?

Explain your thinking.

> **HINT:** You may find it useful to organise your results in a table.

15

NEWS ABOUT GAGARIN-GOLD GETS OUT ...

TEACHER'S NOTES

Curriculum Focus

1. Interpret and present discrete data and continuous data using appropriate graphical methods, including bar charts and time graphs.
2. Estimate, compare and calculate different measures, including money in pounds and pence.
3. Solve problems involving converting between hours and minutes.

Running the Activity

Background

Do the children have regular opportunities to interpret data presented in different ways? How confident are they to discuss the information it is presenting and make estimates about unknown values?

Can they explain why a time graph might be used and what type of data it could present?

Do they understand the importance of reading a scale accurately and identifying the intervals used so that a range of values, including those on unlabelled increments, can be calculated? How confident are they converting between pence and pounds when calculating?

These tasks require children to solve a range of problems using discrete data and a time graph.

◭ Starting Off

Within *Starting Off*, children use the possible scales given to find values for a bar on the bar chart. They will also need to find an unlabelled value by finding the midway point between two increments.

> *Key knowledge:* It is important to check the scale on a chart, graph or any other graphic representation of data so you can read it accurately.

◁ Away We Go

Within *Away We Go*, children move on to identify the actual scale for the bar chart and then answer questions about it. The problem extends to include money and time, where it is necessary to convert between minutes and hours, and between pence and pounds.

> *Key knowledge:* Time graphs are used to represent continuous data that changes over time. Values between labelled points can also be interpreted on the line.

▷ Free Running

Within *Free Running*, children are presented with a time graph about the estimated value of 'Gagarin-gold'. They will need to find values of unlabelled points on the graph and use the information to scale the price accordingly to calculate the value for 7 g at a given time.

In *S.I.D.'s Challenge*, they will need to estimate values on the line graph that are between points. They should explain the decisions they have made.

Sharing Results and Evaluating

Look for children who draw upon knowledge of number lines to use and identify intervals on a scale. Look for those who confidently convert between units of time, and units of money.

Share decisions about the time graph and possible values on the line. Discuss reasons for children's choices for the 9 p.m. value and decide how this may change again at 10 p.m.

Answers

Starting Off
1. a) 4500; b) 5400; c) 7500
2. a) 6750; b) 8100; c) 11,250

Away We Go
1. 8000 ÷ 5 = 1600
2. M (4800); T (7200); W (8800); F (12,000)
3. Monday (4800) and Wednesday (8800)
4. *The Daily Spread* 3500 copies
   Today is the Day! 2850 copies
5. *The Daily Spread* (3500 × 60p) = £2100
   Today is the Day! (2850 × 45p) = £1282.50

Free Running
1.

8 a.m.	10 a.m.	12 p.m.	2 p.m.	4 p.m.	6 p.m.	8 p.m.
£20	£28	£24	£40	£52	£60	£64

2. £52 × 7 = £364

S.I.D.'s Challenge
Children's estimates, but most are likely to be halfway between the known values, e.g. 9 a.m. is halfway between 8 a.m. and 10 p.m. so value estimated is halfway between £20 and £28.

	9 a.m.	11 a.m.	3 p.m.	7 p.m.
1 g	£24	£26	£46	£62
7 g	£168	£182	£322	£ 434

9 p.m. – children's own values with reasonable explanation, e.g. £66 at 9 p.m. as there was an increase of £4 between 6 p.m. and 8 p.m. so another hour on could be £2 more.

THE ROVER BREAKS DOWN
Solving problems about negative and positive numbers.

➤ It is never much fun breaking down, but imagine what it would be like on Mars …
The Mariners have been out collecting samples and exploring new places.
Suddenly, there is a loud bang and the Rover grinds to a halt.

△ Starting Off

What was that?
Why are we not
moving anymore?

The Mariners try to call S.I.D. back at base, but they just get
a 'beeping' sound over the communicator …
The beeps on the first call came **after** every **twelve seconds**. The gap between
the beeps on the second call was **five seconds longer** than on the first call.

1. How long was each call if the Mariners heard 12 'beeps' each time? Write tl
   used to help you.

2. The third call lasted for 72 seconds and again they heard 12 beeps. How long was the gap between
   the beeps this time?
   Ceri knew the answer to this question without having to work it out. How do you think she knew?
   'Ceri knows because …'

◁ Away We Go

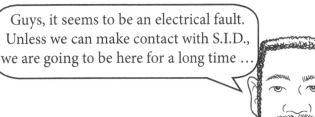

Guys, it seems to be an electrical fault.
Unless we can make contact with S.I.D.,
we are going to be here for a long time …

Dara takes a look at the Rover's engine to see if
he can work out what has gone wrong. If they are
going to be there into the night, Dara wants to find
out about how cold it could get.
These are the temperatures recorded by the Rover's
computer from the warmer part of the day to the coldest:

Day 1 22°C, 17°C, 12°C, 7°C, 2°C, -3°C, -8°C   **Day** 2 19°C, 13°C, 7°C, 1°C, -5°C, -11°C

1. The temperature on Day 1 continues to drop by the same amount each time. Complete the sequence
   of temperatures for Day 1.

2. The temperature on Day 2 also drops by the same amount each time. Complete the sequence
   for Day 2 and find out how much colder the lowest temperature is than 19°C.

Zack and Jade are busy trying to get the communicator to work. They remember that each dial should be pointing to a **different** number, but they all seem to be pointing to zero.

Hold on, I also remember that only the **first** and **last** dials pointed to negative numbers.

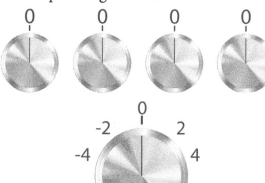

Zack also remembers that the largest number is **eight more** than the smallest number on the dials.

3. Use Jade and Zack's information to find what numbers could have been on the four dials. Try to find some different solutions.

HINT: Try to organise your work to help you find different solutions.

4. Are there any numbers that cannot be on one of the dials? Why?

▷ Free Running

It is starting to get dark and the rest of the Mariners are also getting worried about the temperature at night on Mars. It is a harsh, cold world …

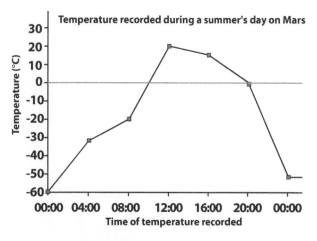

1. Use the time graph to help write at least **five** different statements about the temperature on a summer's day on Mars.

Try to describe how many degrees (°C) the temperature rises and falls by during the day.

S.I.D.'s Challenge

Luckily the Mariners have special suits and emergency gear to keep them warm, but it is still an extremely cold night!

Here are the temperatures recorded that night starting from 16:00.

16:00 (15°C)   18:00 (5°C)   20:00 (-5°C)   22:00 (-20°C)   00:00 (-35°C)   02:00 (-45°C)

Use the information given to draw your own time graph of the temperatures that night.

4

THE ROVER BREAKS DOWN

TEACHER'S NOTES

Curriculum Focus

- Count backwards through zero to include negative numbers.
- Solve number and practical problems that involve all of the above and with increasingly large positive and negative numbers.
- Count in multiples (e.g. 6, 7, 9, 25 and 1000).
- Interpret and present continuous data using time graphs.

Running the Activity
Background

Do the children regularly count on and back in steps of a constant size from zero and from any given number?

What experience do they have of counting back into negative numbers and discussing how patterns might change? (e.g. counting back in tens from 26 results in 26, 16, 6, -4, -14, -24 … – the value of the units digit changes even though we are counting back in tens!)

Do they relate negative numbers to temperature and discuss how temperature changes? Have they seen and interpreted continuous data on time graphs (line graphs) and do they understand how this differs from discrete data?

These tasks require children to work with sequences of positive and negative numbers.

△ Starting Off

Within *Starting Off*, children should recognise that the problem asks them to think about counting in regular steps from zero, i.e. multiples of 12, 17 and 6.

> **Key knowledge:** Counting from zero in steps of a constant will produce a string of multiples of the step size.

◁ Away We Go

Within *Away We Go*, children move on to solve problems involving positive and negative numbers; firstly within a decreasing sequence and then as part of a logic puzzle.

> **Key knowledge:** When counting from positive to negative numbers and vice versa, we must remember to count zero.

▷ Free Running

Within *Free Running*, children are asked to interpret a time graph and create a range of statements about the temperatures shown, including comparisons.

In *S.I.D.'s Challenge* they are given a set of temperatures to be represented on a time graph. They should consider the scale needed to accommodate all values.

Sharing Results and Evaluating

Look for children who confidently count on and back through zero and can reason about any patterns they see. Look for accurate use of language to interpret and discuss the time graphs.
Begin to look at other ways time graphs can be used, particularly in science.

Answers
Starting Off
1. 144 seconds (12 × 12)
   204 seconds (17 × 12)
2. Six seconds
   'Ceri knows because 72 seconds is half of 144 seconds so the gap must also have been half of 12 seconds.'

Away We Go
1. 22°C, 17°C, 12°C, 7°C, 2°C, -3°C, -8°C
2. 19°C, 13°C, 7°C, 1°C, -5°C, -11°C
   -11°C is 30°C lower than 19°C.
3. -6, 0, 2, -4 in any order as long as the negative numbers are first and last
   -4, 0, 4, -2 in any order as long as the negative numbers are first and last
4. -8 and 8 cannot be on the dials as we know the difference between the largest and smallest number is eight. In both these cases, it is not possible to have two negative numbers.
   Six cannot be on the dial for the same reasons as this would only allow one negative number (-2).

Free Running
1. Statements may include, for example:
   The temperature drops by … between … and …
   The temperature rises by … between … and …
   The difference between the lowest and highest temperature that day is …
   The temperature at … was … higher/lower than at …
   There were … temperatures recorded above 0°C
   At … the temperature was …
   The temperature drops very quickly between … and …

S.I.D.'s Challenge
Children's own line graph. The scale should go from at least 15°C to -45°C. This is likely to be in intervals of 5°C. The time line will start from 16:00.

BACK TO BASE
Solving problems about time.

➤ Finally, with the Rover now working again, the Mariners get back to base.

 **Starting Off**

15:35

The digital clock shows the exact time that the Mariners left base on the previous day. They returned at 1:18 a.m. on the following day.

1. Calculate how long they were away from base.

2. How long would they have been away if these times were on Earth?

> Mariners, Earth Control has been very worried about you. You have been missing for a long time …

HINT: Remember that on Mars a day has approximately 24 hours and 39½ minutes.

 **Away We Go**

The journey back from the scene of the breakdown was exactly the same length of time as the journey out to the same place on the previous day.

Use this information and Dara's statement to find out:

1. How long did it take to drive back to base?

2. At what time was the Rover finally fixed?

Remember to show how you worked out your solutions.

> S.I.D., the Rover broke down and it took us four hours and 12½ minutes to fix it!

The Mariners start to think about their second year on Mars and all the adventures so far. They soon realise that exactly ⅔ of the second Martian year has already passed!

3. How many days is ⅔ of a Martian year?

4. How can you show this number of days in Earth years and weeks? How does this change for a leap year?

5. How many more weeks and days on Earth will it take before they have completed the second Martian year on Mars?

> **HINT:** Remember that there are 687 days in a Martian year.

▷ Free Running

One of the control panels counts down each day in seconds.

As a new day begins, the display resets to show the number of seconds in a full day.

> **HINT:** There are **exactly** 24 hours, 39 minutes and 35 seconds in a Martian day.

The Martian day (seconds remaining)				
?	?	?	?	?

1. Find the number of seconds that is displayed on the control panel at the **start** of a new day.

2. What would the display show at 2:00 a.m.?

> Investigate the seconds remaining at these times during the day.

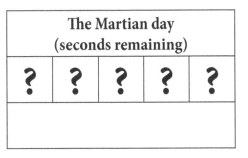

S.I.D.'s Challenge

The Martian day (seconds remaining)				
?	?	?	?	?

02:30   05:00   07:30
10:00   12:30   15:00

Describe any patterns that you notice.

BACK TO BASE

TEACHER'S NOTES

Curriculum Focus

1. Read, write and convert time between analogue and digital 12- and 24-hour clocks.
2. Solve problems involving converting from hours to minutes; minutes to seconds; years to months; weeks to days.

Running the Activity

Background

How frequently do the children discuss time displayed in different ways? Do they understand how the 24-hour clock relates to the 12-hour clock?

How familiar are the children with converting from hours to minutes; minutes to seconds; years to months and weeks to days?

Can they confidently calculate time intervals using a methods such as a number line?

How secure is their understanding of place value when calculating the product of multiples of 10 or 100?

These tasks require children to solve a range of problems involving time on Mars and time on Earth.

◢ Starting Off

Within *Starting Off*, children are comparing a time showed on the 24 hour clock with one using a.m. notation. They must calculate the time intervals on Earth and on Mars.

> *Key knowledge:* Time intervals can be efficiently calculated on the number line by counting up to the next boundary, e.g. up to the next minute or up to the next hour.

◁ Away We Go

Within *Away We Go,* children move on to solve a more complex problem involving subtraction and division. The problems become more challenging as they must consider how minutes and hours, and then days, weeks and years relate to each other when calculating.

> *Key knowledge:* There is exactly 365.242 days in a year, so every four years a leap year occurs to make up the additional day. Therefore, we have 365 days in a year and 366 in a leap year.

▷ Free Running

Within *Free Running*, children are challenged to work in seconds to help investigate the countdown displayed

They are required to use knowledge of multiplying multiples of ten as part of this problem along with subtraction.

In *S.I.D.'s Challenge*, children are required to describe patterns to help find solutions to the problems posed.

Sharing Results and Evaluating

Look for children who use appropriate methods to calculate time intervals.

Look for those that securely draw on knowledge of relationships between units of time to help solve problems.

Share the patterns found in *S.I.D.'s Challenge* and investigate other times in seconds across the day,

Answers
Starting Off
1. 10 hours 22½ minutes
2. 9 hours 43 minutes

Away We Go
1. 3 hours 5 minutes. (10 hrs 22½ mins – 4hrs 12½ mins)/2
2. 10:52^{50} p.m. or 22:52^{50}
   Left at 15:35 and drove for 3 hours 5 minutes (18:40) when it broke down. It took 4 hours 12½ minutes to fix, so finally fixed at 22:52^{50}.
3. 458 days
4. 1 year 93 days so 1 year 13 weeks 2 days
   1 year 92 days so 1 year 13 weeks 1 day (leap year)
5. 229 days so 32 weeks and 5 days

Free Running
1. 88,775 seconds
2. 81,575 seconds

S.I.D.'s Challenge
02:30	79,775 seconds remaining
05:00	70,775 seconds remaining
07:30	61,775 seconds remaining
10:00	52,775 seconds remaining
12:30	43,775 seconds remaining
15:00	34,775 seconds remaining

Each time given is 2 hours 30 minutes later than the one before.
The number of seconds is decreasing by 9000 as this is the number of seconds in every 2 hours 30 minutes.
The HTU value each time is the same, as a multiple of one thousand is being subtracted.

WATER ON MARS?
Solving problems about measurement.

➤ Water on Mars exists as water-ice and dry-ice. It is found in the polar ice caps and under the shallow Martian surface.
Scientists have known for some time that liquid water did once exist on Mars, but because the atmosphere became much colder and thinner, it cannot exist on the Martian surface for any length of time ...

△ Starting Off

The Mariners set off knowing they will be away for many days. They are quite close to the Northern polar ice cap, but they still have a long, long journey ahead of them ...

The Rover travels 45 km every hour. How far will the Mariners have travelled after:
1. four hours and 30 minutes in the Rover?
2. nine hours in the Rover?
3. 18 hours in the Rover?
4. 30 hours in the Rover?

5. Now, write each of these distances in **metres**.

> Attention, Mariners! We need to find out more about water here on Mars. Scientists are still not sure if it once was drinkable. You will need to drive to the polar ice caps to analyse samples of water-ice and dry-ice.

HINT: Remember to use what you know about the relationship between **metres** and **kilometres**.

◁ Away We Go

1. What is the total distance from Base to the Northern polar cap? After 30 hours of travelling, they are still only a **third** of the way there. The Mariners continue their journey for many hours, but finally stop for a rest. Dara spots something interesting ...

> Hey, guys, look at this! The rocks here are a lighter colour and are flat. I wonder if these are similar to the ones found on Mars that contain clay minerals? Clay is a sign that water was once here, and that you could drink the water!

2. The Mariners collect samples from some of the rocks and label them carefully. Complete the label.

Rock samples - evidence of clay?

Distance from base: 1710 km

Hours travelled: _____

After many, many hours of travelling the Mariners finally reach their destination … the polar ice cap!

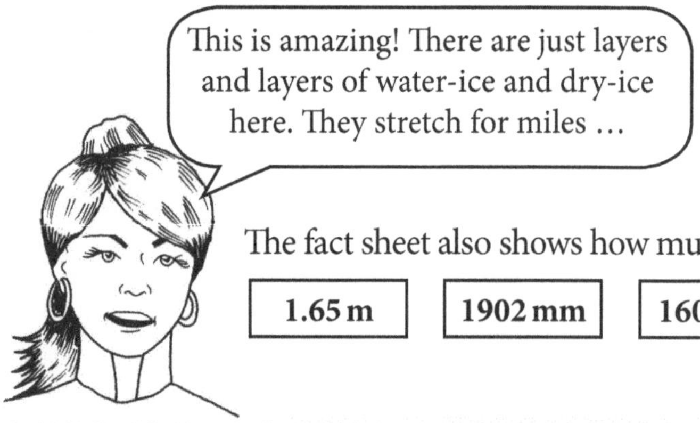

This is amazing! There are just layers and layers of water-ice and dry-ice here. They stretch for miles …

The Mariners look at some of the information they have about the dry-ice.

The fact sheet also shows how much the ice cap grew in five different winters on Mars.

| 1.65 m | 1902 mm | 160.5 cm | 1.92 m | 1600 mm |

Northern Polar Ice Cap Fact sheet

Each winter the ice cap grows by 1.5 m to 2 m of dry-ice. This is frozen carbon dioxide.

In the summer, this dry-ice turns from a solid to a gas and goes into the atmosphere.

3. Order these measurements starting with the winter when the ice cap grew the **least**.

Use what you know about different units of measurement to prove that you are correct.

▷ Free Running

The Mariners stay at the Northern polar ice cap for several days to analyse dry-ice and water-ice.

If only this water-ice could stay as liquid water when melted …

We still don't know if we would be able to drink it even if it did stay as liquid water!

Zack decides to do some calculations anyway, just for fun …

He knows that his specimen jars hold exactly 175 ml of water. He thinks that if he fills a jar with water-ice he might get approximately 175 ml of liquid water.

1. How many specimen jars would he need to fill to get 1.4 litres of liquid water?

2. If Zack adds another eight jars to the 1.4 litres of liquid water, how much liquid water would he have now?

3. Continue adding eight jars at a time and describe any patterns you find. Try to show your findings in litres and millilitres.

HINT: Putting your results in a table may help you to spot pattern

S.I.D.'s Challenge

The Mariners spent exactly 72¼ hours at the polar ice cap.
It took them 225 minutes longer to get back from the ice cap than it took to get there.

1. Using everything that you know so far, calculate how many hours the Mariners were away from base.

2. Approximately how many days was this?

WATER ON MARS?

TEACHER'S NOTES

Curriculum Focus

1. Convert between different units of measure (e.g. kilometre to metre; hours to minutes; litres to millilitres).
2. Estimate, compare and calculate different measures.
3. Order and compare numbers beyond 1000.
4. Solve number and practical problems that involve place value with increasingly large positive numbers and solve scaling problems using multiplication and division.

Running the Activity
Background

How secure are the children using place value to multiply and divide numbers by 10, 100 and 1000? How confidently can they explain the effect on the digits and the use of zero as a place holder?

What experience do they have of working with measure and applying knowledge of place value to make sense of the value of each digit, particularly for decimals?

Can they confidently draw upon the relationships between different units of measure to help them compare, order or calculate effectively?

These tasks require children to work with length, time and capacity.

Starting Off

Within *Starting Off*, children use the given statement to scale a value relating to kilometres travelled in every hour. They should also make use of doubles to help them.

Key knowledge: There are 1000 metres in a kilometre.

Away We Go

Within *Away We Go*, children move on to using their knowledge of division to identify the number of hours taken. The problem extends to ordering lengths (height in this case) shown in centimetres, metres and millimetres.

Key knowledge: It is much easier to compare measurements expressed in the same unit so it is important to know the relationships between them.

Free Running

Within *Free Running*, children are working with capacity and investigating a 'What if …?' scenario that involves scaling amounts and expressing values in litres and millilitres.

In *S.I.D.'s Challenge*, the focus returns to time as children are required to use what they know to calculate a total value in hours and give an approximate value in days.

Sharing Results and Evaluating

Look for children who confidently use place value to convert between units of measurement.

Look for those who make errors by not realising that values are in different units.

Research additional information about the size of polar ice caps, considering values shown and converting between different units of measurement.

Answers
Starting Off

1. 202.5 km
2. 405 km
3. 810 km
4. 1350 km
5. 202,500 m, 405,000 m, 810,000 m, 1,350,000 m

Away We Go

1. 4050 km
2. 38 hours
3. 1600 mm, 160.5 cm, 1.65 m, 1902 mm, 1.92 m
   Convert between different units of measurement so it is easier to compare (e.g. there are 10 mm in a cm so 160.5 cm is 1605 mm, which is 5 mm more than 1600 mm).

Free Running

1. 8 jars
2. 2.8 litres or 2800 ml
3.

8 jars	16 jars	24 jars	32 jars	40 jars	48 jars
1.4 litres	2.8 litres	4.2 litres	5.6 litres	7 litres	8.4 litres
1400 ml	2800 ml	4200 ml	5600 ml	7000 ml	8400 ml

The totals increase by 1.4 litres each time or by 1400 ml.
The number of jars are all multiples of 8.

S.I.D.'s Challenge

90 hours (30 hours was only a third of the way there) + 72¼ hours (at ice cap) + 33¾ hours (30hrs +225 mins) return = 256 hours

Approximately eight days (Earth days or Martian days).

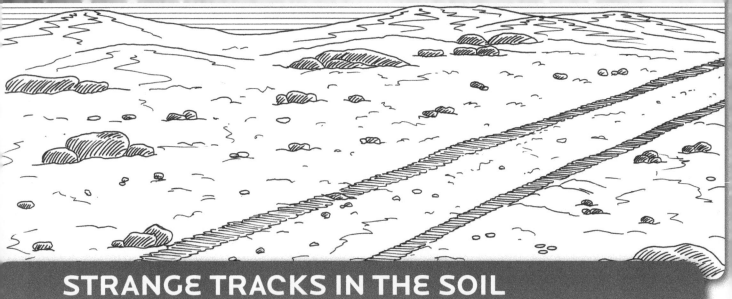

STRANGE TRACKS IN THE SOIL
Solving problems about two-dimensional shapes and symmetry.

➤ **The Mariners spend a lot of time out and about in the Rover, but today was very different.**

◭ Starting Off

As the Mariners make their way back to base, they come across something rather unexpected …

1. The Mariners can see many triangles in the tracks. Name the different triangles they can see and write down how many there are of each.

2. Jade thinks that the other shapes do not belong to the same family as each other. Name the other shapes and explain why Jade has made a mistake. *'Jade has made a mistake because …'*

> **HINT:** Use what you know about the properties of 2-D shapes to help you explain.

Hey, what's that in the soil? There are some very strange tracks over there …

They look like tyre tracks of some kind!

◁ Away We Go

Some of the shapes from the tracks have been sorted in this Carroll Diagram. The labels from the Carroll Diagram are missing.

1. Write some possible labels for the diagram and explain your choice. Is there more than one possibility?

2. Using your labels, describe a shape that could replace the '**?**'.
   Can the '**?**' be any of the other shapes in the tracks? Why?

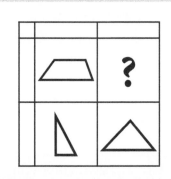

> **HINT:** Remember that in a Carroll Diagram, we use the term '**no**' or '**no**', e.g. grey and not grey.

3. Now think about the labels you will need to place **all** the different shapes from the tracks into this Venn Diagram.

Draw your own Venn Diagram and, using the numbers shown, show where the shapes will go.

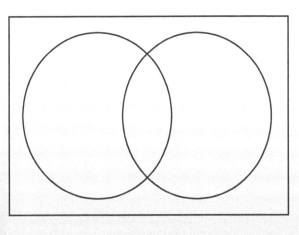

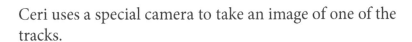

(1)   (2)   (3)   (4)   (5)

▷ Free Running

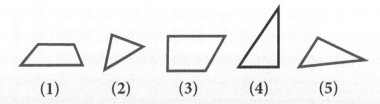

I wonder what made these tracks? Each track appears to have a line of symmetry …

Ceri uses a special camera to take an image of one of the tracks.

With a bit of computer trickery, a new image is created on the screen to show the image reflected in the mirror line shown.

1. Sketch the image that appeared on the screen after it has been reflected.

Did the track have a line of symmetry?

2. What new shapes have been created by the reflection? Make a list of their names.

> **HINT:** Use a mirror or tracing paper to help you. Remember to use a ruler to make your drawing accurate.

S.I.D.'s Challenge

Create a tyre track of your own that has **two lines of symmetry**.

Use at least **two different** 'families' of shapes, e.g. pentagons (regular and irregular) and triangles (scalene, isosceles, etc.)

Remember to show the two lines of symmetry. Please use a ruler.

STRANGE TRACKS IN THE SOIL

TEACHER'S NOTES

Curriculum Focus

1. Compare and classify geometric shapes, including quadrilaterals and triangles, based on their properties and sizes.
2. Identify lines of symmetry in 2-D shapes presented in different orientations.
3. Complete a symmetric figure with respect to a specific line of symmetry.

Running the Activity

Background

What experience do children have of discussing the properties of different triangles and other irregular shapes? Do they recognise that the property of a shape remains the same even when it is in a different orientation?

Do they use mirrors or tracing paper effectively to explore lines of symmetry? Do they recognise that lines of symmetry may not be vertical or horizontal?

Do they regularly use sorting diagrams to categorise numbers, shapes and other data by their properties?

These tasks require children to investigate less familiar shapes and sort them accordingly.

Starting Off

Within *Starting Off*, children identify different triangles and describe the properties of trapezia.

Key knowledge: Triangles can be sorted according to their properties. These include scalene, isosceles, equilateral and right-angled. Both the scalene and isosceles triangle can also be right-angled.

Away We Go

Within *Away We Go*, children move on to decide how the 2-D shapes have been sorted, provide labels and suggest another shape that suits the criteria chosen.

They firstly work with a Carroll Diagram and then a Venn Diagram.

Key knowledge: Regular polygons have the same number of lines of symmetry as sides (e.g. a square has four sides and four lines of symmetry; a regular pentagon has five sides and five lines of symmetry).

Free Running

Within *Free Running*, children are asked to reflect a shape in a vertical mirror line and complete the symmetric figure. They must also look for any new shapes created.

In *S.I.D.'s Challenge*, they should use their experiences from the previous task to create a 'track' that has two lines of symmetry.

Sharing Results and Evaluating

Look for children that draw on their knowledge of the properties of 2-D shapes to identify, describe and sort shapes.

Share the children's own tracks and check for lines of symmetry. Look for symmetry in art work and architecture and discuss the patterns seen.

Answers
Starting Off

1. isosceles (2), scalene (10), right-angled (6)
   Note that right-angled triangles are also scalene.
2. Trapezia
   'Jade has made a mistake because both shapes are trapezia because they have four sides and two of these sides are parallel.'

Away We Go

1. Labels could be:
   trapezium, not trapezium
   line of symmetry, no line of symmetry
   or
   not triangle, triangle
   no line of symmetry, line of symmetry
   or
   4 straight sides (quadrilateral), not 4 straight sides
   line of symmetry, no line of symmetry
2.

   The '?' cannot be another shape from the track.
3. Labels e.g. quadrilaterals/right angles; triangles/right angles. Answer in a Venn diagram.

Free Running

1. The track has no line of symmetry.
2. Irregular pentagons, isosceles triangles, (trapezium, but in same place in original design)

S.I.D.'s Challenge

Children's own examples checked with a mirror.
Two lines of symmetry drawn.

A CLOSE ENCOUNTER WITH THE *CURIOSITY* ROVER
Solving problems about fractions.

➤ NASA's Mars *Curiosity* Rover is on a mission of its very own! It is a Science Laboratory sent to investigate what the Martian environment is like and what it was like in the past, but there are no Mariners to drive it.

△ Starting Off

Mars *Curiosity* Rover Data Screen:	
Launched	Nov 2011
Landed	Aug 2012
Location	Gale Crater
Length of mission on Mars	23 months
Size (approx)	10 feet long
	9 feet wide
	7 feet tall

Wow, that means there is **just under half** of the mission length left to go!

Hey, guys, look at all these interesting facts about *Curiosity*.

1. The mission length on Mars is just under two years. Complete this fraction number sentence
   Mission length is $\boxed{\frac{?}{?}}$ of two years.

2. The *Curiosity* Rover has already been on Mars for **11 months**. What fraction is this of the **whole** mission on Mars?

3. Do you agree with Zack's statement? Explain your thinking.
   'I agree with Zack's statement because …'
   'I disagree with Zack's statement because …'

◁ Away We Go

The Mariners decide to compare the dimensions of their Rover with *Curiosity*.

1. What is Jade comparing?

2. Use Jade's statement to help compare the other measurements. Write statements in the same way.

3. *Curiosity* is 9 ft wide and the *Martian* Rover is 10 ft wide. How can Jade re-write her statement showing a fraction that uses the dimensions in **centimetres**?

HINT: The imperial measurement of **one foot (ft)** is approximately equal to 30 cm.

That means that Curiosity is ⁹⁄₁₀ of the _____ of our rover!

Martian Rover	
Size (approx)	16 ft long
	10 ft wide
	8 ft tall

Martian Rover	
Arm Reach	12 ft
Weight	1200 kg
Number of wheels	10

Here are some more measurements for the *Martian* Rover.

The 'arm' on the rover holds and moves the tools that help scientists get up close to the rocks and soils. The Mariners use their 'arm' when rocks are out of reach.

4. Use the clues below to find out the same measurements for *Curiosity*.

a) Arm reach of *Curiosity* is ⁷⁄₁₂ of the *Martian* Rover.
b) Weight of *Curiosity* is ¾ of the *Martian* Rover.
c) *Curiosity* has ⅗ of the number of wheels.

▷ Free Running

Come on, let's get going I can't wait to see *Curiosity*!

The Mariners are excited to see *Curiosity* and head off to Gale Crater.

The shaded part of the bar below shows the fraction of the distance the Mariners have driven so far.

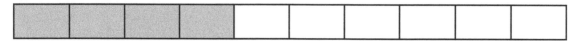

1. What fraction of the journey do the Mariners have left to drive?

2. The Mariners drive a further $\frac{25}{100}$ of the total journey. Draw the fraction bar now.

3. How many **hundredths** do the Mariners still need to drive? Can this fraction be written in a different way?

HINT: Think about how you can use equivalent fractions.

S.I.D.'s Challenge

Finally the Mariners reach Gale Crater, but there seems to be a problem …
Curiosity usually sends a message to Earth each day with results of its investigations, but not today!

Here is the number of samples collected by *Curiosity* in the past **four days**.

	Day 1	Day 2	Day 3	Day 4	Day 5
Rock samples	16	28	24	36	?
Soil samples	24	10	36	40	?

1. What fractions of the samples are of **rocks** on each day?

2. ⅝ of the samples were of rocks on **day five**. *Curiosity* collected 40 samples in total.
What information should *Curiosity* have sent to Earth?

A CLOSE ENCOUNTER WITH THE *CURIOSITY* ROVER
TEACHER'S NOTES

Curriculum Focus

1. Count up and down in hundredths; recognise that hundredths arise when dividing an object by a hundred and dividing tenths by ten.
2. Solve problems involving increasingly harder fractions to calculate quantities, and fractions to divide quantities, including non-unit fractions where the answer is a whole number.

Running the Activity
Background

How confidently do the children draw on multiplication and division facts to help find unit and non-unit fractions of amounts?
Can they also draw on these facts to find strings of equivalent fractions?

Do the children recognise how a comparison can be shown as a fraction, e.g. to compare the number of samples collected on day one (four) to day two (five) a fraction of $\frac{4}{5}$ can be used.

Can they explain the relationship between tenths and hundredths? This is also in preparation for calculating with decimal numbers.

These tasks require children to represent fractions and interpret fractions of amounts.

△ Starting Off

Within *Starting Off*, children create fractions drawing on the information given. They must first decide on the value of the whole. They will also be required to reason and compare a less familiar fraction with a half.

Key knowledge: When finding fractions of an amount we need to know how much the 'whole' is worth.

◁ Away We Go

Within *Away We Go*, children move on to find fractions by comparing different values. The problem extends to find fractions of amounts to identify the measurements of the *Curiosity* Rover.

Key knowledge: We can create a fraction by knowing 'how much of' or 'out of' how many is represented, i.e. 5 out of 8 is $\frac{5}{8}$.

▷ Free Running

Within *Free Running*, children are presented with an image of a fraction related to tenths. They are required to convert tenths to hundredths as the problem develops.
They must also check to see whether any of the fractions can be written in a different way using knowledge of equivalent fractions.

In *S.I.D.'s Challenge*, they are required to identify the whole, i.e. the total number of samples collected, so that the fraction of rock samples can be found.

Sharing Results and Evaluating

Look for children who confidently draw on multiplication and division facts to find unit and non-unit fractions of amounts.

Look for those who can explain why a given fraction represents a relationship between two values, i.e. measurements in this case.

Share results for *S.I.D.'s Challenge* and discuss the importance of identifying the 'whole' when working with fractions.

Answers
Starting Off
1. Mission length is $\frac{23}{24}$ of two years.
2. $\frac{11}{23}$
3. 'I disagree with Zack because there is $\frac{12}{23}$ left of the mission and this is just over ½. Half of 23 is 11.5 not 12.'

Away We Go
1. Width
2. *Curiosity* is $\frac{10}{16}$ (⅝) of the length of our Rover!
   Curiosity is ⅞ of the height of our Rover!
3. *Curiosity* is $\frac{270}{300}$ of the width of our Rover!
4. Arm 7 ft, weight 900 kg, six wheels

Free Running
1. $\frac{6}{10}$ or ⅗
2. 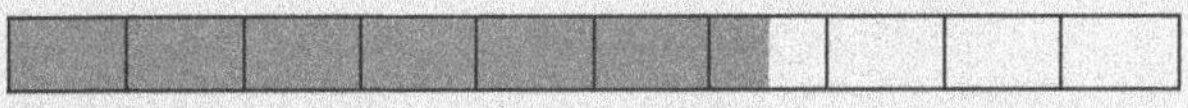
3. $\frac{35}{100}$ or $\frac{7}{20}$

S.I.D.'s Challenge
Day 1 rock samples = $\frac{16}{40}$ or ⅖
Day 2 rock samples = $\frac{28}{38}$ or $\frac{14}{19}$
Day 3 rock samples = $\frac{24}{60}$ or ⅖
Day 4 rock samples = $\frac{36}{76}$ or $\frac{9}{19}$

Day 5 ⅝ of 40 is 25 so 25 are rock samples and 15 are soil samples.

LIFE ON MARS?
Solving problems about addition and subtraction.

➤ The Mariners have read many stories about possible life on Mars and decide to investigate for evidence of life in the Martian environment.

◢ Starting Off

> I think that the craters are a good place to start as we can drill down to some of the older rocks.

The Mariners begin to pack the tools they need for the trip.
They will take three rock-drills of different lengths (**A, B** and **C**) for the dig.
They will place them carefully in a larger box.

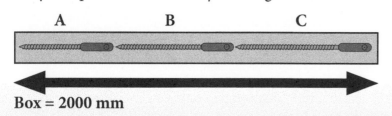

A   **B**   **C**

Box = 2000 mm

The lengths of the drills can be found using the following number sentences:

> **A** + 1045 mm = 1506 mm
>
> **Box – C** = 1118 mm
>
> **B** + 247 mm = **C**

1. Calculate the length of each drill A, B and C. Show your working.
2. How much space is left in the length of the box?

◁ Away We Go

> We must decide what else we want to take and how much space we will need.

324 mm

190 mm Small tools

475 mm

Food   296 mm   800 mm

290 mm   Specimen jars

Jade and Ceri are arranging these boxes in different ways.

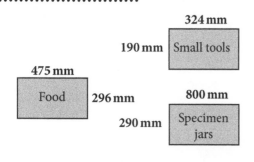

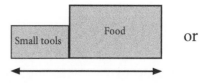

Small tools   Food   or   Small tools

Food

1. What different total lengths can you make by arranging pairs of boxes in this way?
2. Now try all three boxes together.

Spare battery for Rover	460 mm
703 mm	

	2000 mm	
271 mm	Rock-drills	

The Mariners continue to work out different lengths when placing two boxes together like this.

?   **?**

Unfortunately, they forget to write down the boxes they use each time!

> We must not forget to pack the drills and the spare battery for the Rover.

Boxes	A	B	Specimen jars	C
A		2475 mm	? mm	1178 mm
B	2475 mm		2800 mm	2703 mm
Specimen jars	1275 mm	2800 mm		1503 mm
C	1178 mm	? mm	1503 mm	

3. Use the information given to find the names of the mystery boxes **A**, **B** and **C**.

4. Now fill in any missing information.

▷ Free Running

The Mariners start to pack the storage space of the Rover with the five boxes they need to take with them.

But there seems to be a bit of a problem; they can't fit it all in! Jade and Ceri think that there must be a better way to do it …

1. Find a way to place all the boxes in the storage space of the Rover. Draw and label your idea, showing measurements of the boxes and any spare space.

> Mariners, you will need to pack the Rover very carefully to make sure that everything fits in. You must also remember there is not enough room to stack boxes on top of each other!

	Storage space in the Rover	
760 mm		

2000 mm

> **HINT:** Remember that you have already done some calculations that may help you!

S.I.D.'s Challenge

Jade and Ceri finally work out a way to make everything fit.

They find that they still have a little bit of space for a **box of snacks**.

Using your own drawing and measurements from before, find out the **maximum** size of the snack box.

LIFE ON MARS?

TEACHER'S NOTES

Curriculum Focus

1. Add and subtract numbers with up to four digits using the efficient written methods of columnar addition and subtraction where appropriate.
2. Estimate and use inverse operations to check answers to a calculation.
3. Solve addition and subtraction two-step problems in contexts, deciding which operations and methods to use and why.

Running the Activity

Background

What experience do the children have of finding and using families of related facts? Can they explain why each number sentence is true?

Do they recognise that four different number sentences can be written using addition and subtraction? Can they explain, however, this will look different when two numbers are the same? i.e. for 75, 75 and 150, produces only two different looking number sentences.

Can the children confidently explain when a written method of addition or subtraction should be applied and when a mental method is more appropriate?

These tasks require children to solve a range of one-step and two-step problems involving addition and subtraction of three- and four-digit numbers.

△ Starting Off

Within *Starting Off*, children will need to use the inverse operation to help calculate values using related facts.

> ***Key knowledge:*** When finding a missing value, knowing how families of related facts work helps to identify the calculation needed.

◁ Away We Go

Within *Away We Go*, children move on to add pairs of three- and four-digit numbers. The problem extends so that the inverse can also be used to find missing values and labels in a comparison table.

> ***Key knowledge:*** Subtraction is the inverse of addition, and vice versa. These operations can be used to 'undo' the effect of each other.

▷ Free Running

Within *Free Running*, children are to investigate possible ways to arrange the boxes within a given space. They should draw on calculations already made and apply strategies of addition, subtraction and the inverse to explore solutions.

S.I.D.'s Challenge is an extension of the previous problem where children are to interpret the unlabelled dimensions of their own design to calculate a maximum value for an additional box.

Sharing Results and Evaluating

Look for children who confidently reorder number sentences and choose the appropriate operation to calculate a missing value, including the use of the inverse.

Share children's own ideas for packing the storage space and investigate to see whether the boxes can fit into an even smaller space.

Answers
Starting Off

1. A = 461 mm   1506 − 1045 = 461
   B = 635 mm   882 − 247 = 635
   C = 882 mm   2000 − 1118 = 882
2. 22 mm length left in the case.

Away We Go

1. Food and small tools:
   475 mm + 324 mm = 799 mm
   296 mm + 190 mm = 486 mm
   Food and specimen jars:
   475 mm + 800 mm = 1275 mm
   296 mm + 290 mm = 586 mm
   Small tools and specimen jars:
   324 mm + 800 mm = 1124 mm
   190 mm + 290 mm = 480 mm
2. 475 mm + 324 mm + 800 mm = 1599 mm
   296 mm + 190 mm + 290 mm = 776 mm
3. A (food), B (shovels) and C (spare battery)
4. A + specimen jars = 1275 mm
   (same as specimen jars + A)
   C + B = 2703 mm (same as B + C)

Free Running

1. Children's own designs, e.g.

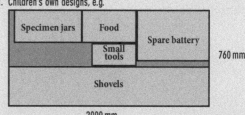

However, there should be other measurements showing sizes of boxes and any spare space.

S.I.D.'s Challenge

Children's own ideas, but related to spare space left on their designs.

AN AMAZING DISCOVERY
Solving problems about fractions.

➤ Scientists on Earth are eager to know more about life on Mars and whether there really is life on other planets in the solar system …

◮ Starting Off ✓

The Mariners are already busy collecting samples from craters. They are each using trays to carry all of the specimen jars.

> Mariners, Earth Control has promised scientists information about samples from the craters here on Mars. You will need to drive out to some of the deepest craters and collect specimens of rocks, dust and soil.

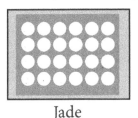
Jade

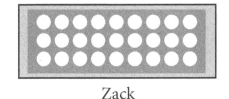
Zack

Jade and Zack have each filled exactly ⅔ of the number of specimen jars in their trays.

1. How many specimen jars have they each filled?

2. Ceri says that they have not both filled ⅔ of their jars. She thinks they have made a mistake because the number of jars filled is not the same. How can you explain to Ceri that she is the one who has made the mistake?

◁ Away We Go   P1 = ✓ P2 = turn over

Zack and Jade each fill another three specimen jars and place them in their trays.

1. What fraction of their whole trays have Zack and Jade collected now?

2. Can either of these fractions be represented in a different way?

> **HINT:** Think about how you can use equivalent fractions to help you.

3. Jade writes a number sentence to work out what fraction of her tray she still has to fill.

$\frac{?}{24} - \frac{?}{24} = \frac{?}{24}$ Complete this number sentence for Jade and write a sentence in the same way for Zack.

Dara has also been busy filling specimen jars in his tray, but Zack does not agree that he has been working as hard.

Hey, Dara, you need to speed up. You have only filled 3/5 of the specimen jars in your tray!

I don't know why you are telling me to speed up. I have filled exactly the same number of specimen jars as you!

4. Do you think that Dara can possibly be correct? Explain your thinking.
  'I think … because …'

5. How many specimen jars are there in total in Dara's tray?

Free Running

Well done, Mariners. The samples must now be carefully analysed.

Having filled all of their specimen jars, the Mariners return to base.

All jars are carefully labelled and placed in one larger tray.
This tray can hold 120 specimen jars in total!

1. What fraction of the larger tray did Jade, Zack and Dara's specimens fill?
  Can this fraction be written in more than one way?

2. Ceri has also placed her jars into the larger tray. The tray is $^{11}/_{12}$ full.
  How many specimen jars did Ceri fill?

3. Ceri had the same size tray as which other Mariner?

S.I.D.'s Challenge

As the last $^1/_5$ of the samples is tested, the lights on the machine begin to flash red and a terrible sounding signal echoes through the M-PODs …

A strange green glow lights up the M-POD … could it be alien bacteria?!

1. How many specimens glowed green?

2. Which Mariner had the contaminated tray?

They are all from my tray! $^{11}/_{12}$ of the specimens in my tray are glowing green!

AN AMAZING DISCOVERY

TEACHER'S NOTES

Curriculum Focus

1. Recognise and show, using diagrams, families of common equivalent fractions.
2. Add and subtract fractions with the same denominator.
3. Solve problems involving increasingly harder fractions to calculate quantities, and fractions to divide quantities, including non-unit fractions where the answer is a whole number.

Running the Activity

Background

Do children recognise when two or more fractions are equivalent? Can they explain why two fractions are equivalent and use this knowledge to help make sense of less familiar sets of equivalent fractions?

What experience do the children have of finding non-unit fractions of amounts beyond their known multiplication tables? Do they recognise the relationship between fractions and division?

Can they describe the relationship of a smaller set to a larger set as a fraction? i.e. recognising or calculating that 16 represents ⅔ of 24.

These tasks also require children to subtract fractions with the same denominator.

Starting Off

Within *Starting Off*, children compare the same fraction of a different whole. They must also reason why the amounts these fractions represent are different.

Key knowledge: When comparing fractions of amounts we need to know how much each 'whole' is worth.

Away We Go

Within *Away We Go*, children move on to identifying equivalent fractions and to comparing fractions that do not share the same denominator. They are also required to make up number sentences using subtraction to help show the fraction left of the whole.

Key knowledge: A string of equivalent fractions can be formed by scaling both the denominator and numerator up or down (× or ÷) by the same amount.

Free Running

Within *Free Running*, children are required to work with more unfamiliar fractions as the denominator is more than one hundred.

They must also interpret a fraction in its simplest form and relate it to the denominator they are working with, i.e. relate twelfths to one-hundred-and-twentieths.

In *S.I.D.'s Challenge* it is important that children recognise that the number of specimens tested is 110 and not 120. Again, the fraction of the whole is given in its simplest form.

Sharing Results and Evaluating

Look for children who use knowledge of multiplication tables and division to identify equivalent fractions. Look for accurate use of mathematical language when explaining thinking and proving decisions.

Share children's working with fractions shown in their simplest form and begin to explore those that cannot be simplified, making connections to factors and prime numbers.

Answers
Starting Off
1. Jade has filled 16 jars and Zack has filled 18.
2. Ceri has made a mistake because they have filled ⅔ of the number of jars they each have. 16 is ⅔ of 24 and 18 is ⅔ of 27.

Away We Go
1. Zack has now filled $21/27$ and Jade $19/24$
2. $21/27$ can also be written as $7/9$

3. $\frac{24}{24} - \frac{19}{24} = \frac{5}{24}$

$\frac{27}{27} - \frac{21}{27} = \frac{6}{27}$ or $\frac{2}{9}$

4. 'I think that Dara can be correct because he may have more specimen jars in his tray than Zack.'
5. 35

Free Running
1. $86/120$ or $43/60$
2. 24
3. Jade

S.I.D.'s Challenge
1. ⅕ of 110 is 22 so 22 jars glowed green.
2. Jade or Ceri because $11/12$ is equivalent to $22/24$.

FOLLOW THE LEADER
Solving problems about fractions and decimals.

> ➤ The four Mariners spend so much time together that they do have the occasional argument, but today things got a little out of hand.

△ Starting Off

The Mariners are having breakfast and talking about what they have done to make the mission to Mars a success.

I discovered what could be alien bacteria!

I found the light flat rocks that contain clay minerals! I also fixed the Rover when we broke down!

So what? I fixed the control panel on *Gagarin 2* and mended the communicator in the Rover!

You didn't mend the communicator on your own Zack, we did that together!

1. How many different 'successes' are mentioned here? What fraction of these is mentioned by each Mariner?
2. How can you explain why these fractions do not total **one** whole?
   'These fractions do not total one whole because …'

◁ Away We Go

Zack is angry because Dara is always asked to check the M-PODS and he can easily do it too. Zack storms off to check the protective frames for the M-PODS instead.
That will make him feel better and he is always much more careful than Dara …
Zack measures the lengths of the steel rods to the nearest centimetre.

Attention, Dara, you need to check that that the growing M-POD is working properly and all screws, bolts and hinges are secure.

2.09 m   2.65 m   1.9 m   3 m

1. Describe the two different values of the digit **9** in **centimetres**.

2. What fraction of a metre is each of these values?

HINT: Remember to use what you know about equivalent fractions.

3. What fraction of a metre longer is 3 m than 2.65 m? Can this fraction be written in more than one way?

Dara reports back to S.I.D. that he only had time to check the following fractions of the bolts, screws and hinges.

| Hinges ⁷/₁₀ | Screws ²/₅ | Bolts ¾ |

4. Which of these is the largest fraction? How do you know?

5. Write each of these fractions as a decimal equivalent and put them in order from smallest to largest.

6. Zack offers to finish checking the growing M-POD. He wants to show that he can do it too!
What **decimal** fraction of the hinges, screws and bolts does he still need to check?

▷ Free Running

Dara is angry that Zack has finished the task that S.I.D. had asked him to do.
Ceri and Jade also get involved as they feel that tasks should be shared and no one is in charge …

Zack, I was in charge of that task. You need to stick to your own tasks and not interfere with mine!

Zack: I have to do ⁴/₁₀ of the cooking.
Jade and Ceri: We share the remaining fraction equally.

Jade: I have to check 76 out of 100 air filters in the growing M-POD.
Ceri: I have to check ¼ of the remaining air filters!
Dara: And I have to check the fraction left!

Dara: I have to do 0.55 of the driving in the Rover!
Zack, Ceri and Jade: And we share the rest of the driving equally!

1. Use all the information given to find out what fraction of the tasks each Mariner does.
   - Look out for any equivalent fractions!
   - Remember to write each fraction as a decimal as well.

2. Show your findings in a table of your choice, but remember to label

S.I.D.'s Challenge

The argument continues as the Mariners compare the fraction of cleaning they each do in the M-PODS.

Ceri: I do **more than double** the amount that you do, Zack!
Jade: I clean ³/₁₀ of the M-PODS.
Dara: I do ⅕ of the cleaning, Jade!
Zack: I do more than ⅛ of the cleaning!

1. What do you know about the fraction of the cleaning done by both Ceri and Zack?

2. What decimal fraction of the **total** cleaning could Ceri do? And Zack? Make a list of possible solutions. Give an example of a solution that is **not** possible and explain why.

FOLLOW THE LEADER

TEACHER'S NOTES

Curriculum Focus

1. Recognise and write decimal equivalents of any number of tenths or hundredths.
2. Recognise and write decimal equivalents to ¼, ½; ¾, etc.
3. Solve simple measure problems involving fractions and decimals to two decimal places.

Running the Activity

Background

What experience do the children have of identifying what fraction of the whole an amount represents?

Do they draw on knowledge of multiplication and division to find strings of equivalent fractions?

Are they secure with the relationship between fractions and division and how this can help to calculate decimal equivalents? e.g. $\frac{3}{10}$ can be written as 3 ÷ 10, which is 0.3.

These tasks require children to work with both fractions and decimals using equivalence to help them solve problems.

Starting Off

Within *Starting Off*, children identify the whole and decide what fraction of the whole each amount represents. They must also reason about the fractions found and their relationship to the whole.

> ***Key knowledge:*** We can create a fraction by knowing 'how much of' or 'out of' how many is represented, i.e. 2 out of 5 is $\frac{2}{5}$.

Away We Go

Within *Away We Go*, children move on to consider fractions and their decimal equivalents. They must also explain the value of the digits in a decimal number. The problem extends to consider fraction pairs to one and decimal complements to a whole.

> ***Key knowledge:*** We can use the relationship between fractions and division to help us find decimal equivalents, e.g. $\frac{7}{100}$ can be written as 7 ÷ 100 which is 0.07.

Free Running

Within *Free Running*, children are given statements about fractions of tasks done by each Mariner. They must use logic to find out missing information and decide how this can best be represented in a table.

In *S.I.D.'s Challenge* they are required to reason about the fractions given and find a range of possibilities to suit criteria for Ceri and Zack.

Sharing Results and Evaluating

Look for children who draw on multiplication and division to simplify or find equivalent fractions. Share children's workings for calculating decimal equivalents and, using a calculator, further explore the relationship between fractions and division to find less familiar decimal equivalents.

Answers

Starting Off

1. Five
   Ceri $\frac{1}{5}$, Dara $\frac{2}{5}$, Zack $\frac{2}{5}$ and Jade $\frac{1}{5}$
2. 'These fractions do not total one whole because the radio was mentioned by two different Mariners and both of these fractions have to be counted to answer the question.'

Away We Go

1. 9 is worth 9 cm in 2.09 m and 90 cm in 2.9 m
2. $\frac{9}{100}$ and $\frac{90}{100}$ ($\frac{9}{10}$)
3. $\frac{35}{100}$ or $\frac{7}{20}$
4. ¾ is largest. $\frac{2}{5}$ is less than a half and $\frac{7}{10}$ is more than a half, but less than ¾ (0.7 is smaller than 0.75)
5. 0.4, 0.7, 0.75
6. 0.6 (screws), 0.3 (hinges) and 0.25 (bolts)

Free Running

1. and 2.

	Jade	Zack	Ceri	Dara
Cooking	$\frac{3}{10}$ or 0.3	$\frac{4}{10}$ ($\frac{2}{5}$) or 0.4	$\frac{3}{10}$ or 0.3	0
Air filters	$\frac{76}{100}$ ($\frac{19}{25}$) or 0.76	0	$\frac{6}{100}$ ($\frac{3}{50}$) or 0.06	$\frac{18}{100}$ ($\frac{9}{50}$) or 0.18
Driving	$\frac{3}{20}$ or 0.15	$\frac{3}{20}$ or 0.15	$\frac{3}{20}$ or 0.15	$\frac{55}{100}$ ($\frac{11}{20}$) or 0.55

S.I.D.'s Challenge

1. Ceri and Zack share ½ of the cleaning
2. The value for Ceri and Zack must sum to 0.5. Possible solutions include:

Zack	Ceri (must be more than double Zack's)
0.126	0.374
0.127	0.373, etc.
0.13	0.37
0.14	0.36
0.15	0.35
0.16	0.34, etc.

(0.17 and 0.34) This example solution is not possible as 0.34 is exactly double and 0.17 and 0.34 sum to 0.51 and not 0.5.

A RIFT OPENS UP
Solving problems about multiplication and division.

➤ The relationship between the Mariners has not been the same since their recent arguments. Soon, members of the team start to take sides and this causes a rift.

△ Starting Off

Jade prepared 28 samples each day that week. Dara prepared the same number in only four days.

1. How many samples did Jade prepare that week? Write down the calculation you used.

2. Dara prepared the same amount on each of his days. How many samples did he prepare each day?
Write down the calculation you used.

3. How many samples did Dara prepare in the whole week?

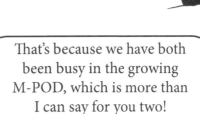

Hey, Zack! Dara and I have prepared more samples for analysis than you this week. The same goes for you too, Ceri!

That's because we have both been busy in the growing M-POD, which is more than I can say for you two!

◁ Away We Go

Zack and Ceri have been busy spraying the plants with feed. The plants sprayed are arranged in equal rows.

Zack sprays 12 rows and Ceri sprays 17 rows.

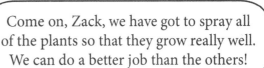

Come on, Zack, we have got to spray all of the plants so that they grow really well. We can do a better job than the others!

1. Ceri calculates the total number of plants she sprayed using these calculations:
$17 \times 20 =$ and $17 \times 4 =$
How many plants are in each row?

2. How many plants did Ceri spray altogether?

3. Zack also worked out the total number of plants he sprayed using two calculations like Ceri. Write the two calculations he used and the total number of plants sprayed.

Mariners, you are all good at your tasks. You must not argue with each other like this; it is not good for the team!

But the Mariners seem to take no notice. They want to prove who has been doing the most tasks in the past **four weeks**.

Ceri:	Zack:	Jade:	Dara:
8 tasks every day of the week.	9 tasks on 6 days of the week and only 4 on the other day.	11 tasks on 5 days of the week and only 1 on each of the other two days.	12 tasks on 4 days of the week and only . on each of the othe three days.

4. Calculate the number of tasks each Mariner did in 4 weeks.

5. Did Jade and Dara do more tasks altogether than Ceri and Zack?

▷ Free Running

Zack and Ceri decide to keep themselves busy and away from the others. They are in the growing M-POD. They have counted groups of sweet potatoes, tomatoes and onions. They used a picture to represent each group.

Mariners, I need you to keep an accurate log about the foods you are growing. You need to record the height of the plants and how much food has been produced so far.

A group of sweet potatoes

A group of tomatoes

A group of onions

Here is some of the information collected so far from just one area of the M-POD:

$$9 \text{🍠} + 10 \text{🧅} = 360 \text{ items}$$

$$13 \text{🍅} = 156 \text{ tomatoes}$$

$$5 \text{🧅} + 5 \text{🍅} = 150 \text{ items}$$

HINT: A number in front of a food tells you how many groups there are, e.g.
$2 \text{🍅} = 2$ groups of tomatoes

1. Use the information to calculate the **number** of tomatoes, sweet potatoes and onions in the groups represented by each picture.

2. How many sweet potatoes were counted altogether?

S.I.D.'s Challenge

Zack and Ceri counted a total of 48 lettuces, 35 garlic bulbs and 72 potatoes in the same area. They counted them in groups of a mystery size.

Use this information to make up a similar problem for your friend or teacher to solve.
Use a picture or a letter, e.g. **L** for lettuce, to represent each group.
They must use your clues to work out the mystery size of each group.

A RIFT OPENS UP

TEACHER'S NOTES

Curriculum Focus

1. Multiply two-digit and three-digit numbers by a one-digit number using formal written layout.
2. Solve problems involving multiplying and dividing, including using the distributive law to multiply two numbers by one digit, integer scaling problems and harder correspondence problems such as n objects are connected to m objects.

Running the Activity

Background

What experience do the children have of scaling amounts up and down for multiplication and division?

Do they recognise when they need to multiply and when they need to divide? Do they have a secure efficient method for each of these operations?

What experience do they have of identifying unknown values that have to suit more than one criteria?

These tasks require the children to use knowledge of multiplication and division to solve a range of different problems.

Starting Off

Within *Starting Off*, children are to identify the required calculation and use an appropriate method of multiplication and division.

> *Key knowledge:* Multiplication is the inverse of division and vice versa.

Away We Go

Within *Away We Go*, children move on to use their knowledge of arrays to calculate the number of plants sprayed.
They go on to solve problems involving more steps.

> *Key knowledge:* To support multiplication, a number can be partitioned using the distributive law so that more efficient or easier calculations can be completed.

 ## Free Running

Within *Free Running*, children are given three different, but related statements and must use the information to find the missing values represented by three symbols.

In *S.I.D.'s Challenge* they use the total values given to create their own problem for others to solve. They must use knowledge of factors to help decide on the group size for each food item.

Sharing Results and Evaluating

Look for children who can explain whether multiplication or division is to be used.

Look for those that draw on known facts and place value before adopting a written method.

Share solutions for *S.I.D.'s Challenge* and consider other problems that work in the same way.

Answers

Starting Off

1. 196 28×7 or 7×28
2. 49 a day $196 \div 4$
3. 343 49×7 or 7×49

Away We Go

1. 24 in a row
2. 408 plants sprayed
3. 12×20 and 12×4
   288 plants sprayed
4. Ceri 224, Zack 232, Jade 228 and Dara 228
5. Each pair did the same number of tasks, i.e. 456 each

Free Running

1. Tomatoes (12 in a group), sweet potatoes (20 in a group) and onions (18 in a group)
2. 180 sweet potatoes

S.I.D.'s Challenge

Children's own solutions, e.g.
$6 L + 5 GB = 83$ items
       $12 P = 72$ potatoes
$3 GB + 10 P = 81$ items

As long as the number of lettuces in each group is a factor of 48, a group of potatoes is a factor of 72 and a group of garlic bulbs is a factor of 35, the children can make up different clues as they like.
However, the clues given must allow the solver to identify the number of items in each group and the amounts should not exceed the totals of 48, 72 and 35 given.

TWO SIDES TO EVERYTHING
Solving problems about perimeter.

➤ After several days full of quarrels, the relationship between the Mariners has really broken down.
Zack and Ceri decide that enough is enough and they are going to separate areas of the Base camp.

▲ Starting Off

Ceri and Zack take some rope from storage
and make plans to use it to create their own areas.
They will each use the rope around their M-PODs.

> Ceri, I think we need some
> space away from the others. We
> could all do with some cooling
> off time …

Ceri plans to make an equilateral triangle with her rope.
Each side will be 7.8 metres (m) long.

1. Calculate the perimeter of the shape that will be made by the rope around Ceri's M-POD.
Write the calculation you used.

Zack will make a rectangle. The rope he will use
for each of the longer sides is 836 cm and for
each of the shorter sides he will use 6.25 m.

2. Calculate the perimeter of the shape that will be
made by the rope around Zack's M-POD.
Write the calculation you used.

> **HINT:** The perimeter is the distance
> (or path) around the edge of
> a 2-D shape.

◁ Away We Go

Jade and Dara have heard what the others are doing and will also make a
rectangular shape around each of their M-PODs with rope.

They used the following calculations to work out how much rope they each needed:

Jade $(2 \times 7.9 \text{ m}) + (2 \times 5.8 \text{ m}) = \boxed{?}$

Dara $(2 \times 720 \text{ cm}) + (2 \times 605 \text{ cm}) = \boxed{?}$

> **HINT:** Brackets ( ) are used here to
> keep parts of the calculation
> together.

1. Draw and label each of the rectangles they plan to make.
2. Calculate the perimeter of each of the rectangles.

Ceri and Zack are pleased with their plans until they realise that it will be more difficult to meet at each other's M-PODs.

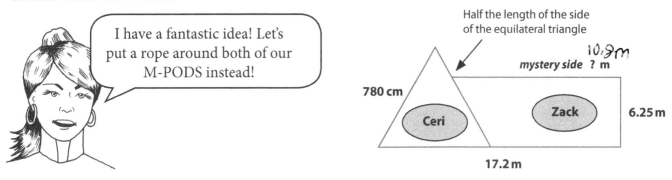

I have a fantastic idea! Let's put a rope around both of our M-PODS instead!

Half the length of the side of the equilateral triangle

10.9m

mystery side ? m

780 cm

Ceri

Zack

6.25 m

17.2 m

Zack used this calculation to work out the length of rope needed for the mystery side:

$$6.4 \text{ m} + \boxed{? \text{ m}} = 17.2 \text{ m}$$

3. What is the length of the mystery side?

4. The length of the piece of rope they have is 45 metres. Do they have enough rope to make this shape around their M-PODs? Prove your decision.

▷ Free Running

Now Jade and Dara are also planning to put ropes around both their M-PODs in the same way. They have a 42.5 metre long piece of rope.

Here are some of the possible designs they have come up with:

a)

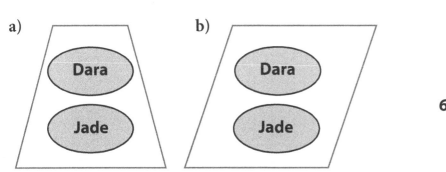

Dara

Jade

b)

Dara

Jade

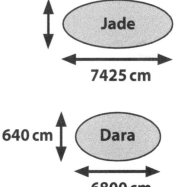

Jade

7425 cm

640 cm Dara

6800 cm

1. Use what you know about the size of Jade and Dara's M-PODS to plan possible measurements for designs A and B using **all** of the rope.

Look out for shapes that have sides of equal length and remember they only have 42.5 metres of rope!

S.I.D.'s Challenge

Jade and Dara decide not to use any of the designs above and choose the one shown here.
They use **only** 42 metres of rope for their design. What are the possible measurements for each side?
Is there a quicker way to calculate the perimeter of this shape? Explain your idea.

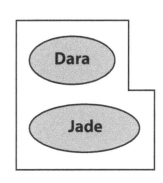

Dara

Jade

TWO SIDES TO EVERYTHING

TEACHER'S NOTES

Curriculum Focus

1. Measure and calculate the perimeter of shapes, including a rectilinear figure (including squares) in centimetres and metres.

Running the Activity
Background

How often are children engaged in investigative tasks involving shape? Can they draw on what they know about the property of shape to help make decisions? Do they use the appropriate language to describe shapes and identify when all or some of the sides are of equal length?

What experience do the children have of finding perimeters of 2-D shapes beyond counting squares? Do they know that the perimeter of a rectilinear shape can be found as long as we know the length of one of each pair of parallel sides?

These tasks also require the application of a range of calculation skills drawing on all four operations.

Starting Off

Within *Starting Off*, children use knowledge of the properties of the rectangle and equilateral triangle to identify the lengths of each side and calculate the perimeter.

> **Key knowledge:** The perimeter is the distance (or path) around the edge of a 2-D shape.

Away We Go

Within *Away We Go*, children move on to making sense of the equation used to find the perimeter of a rectilinear shape and use this to calculate the actual perimeters.

The problem extends to finding the perimeter of an irregular shape using the measurements given and clues to calculate any unknown measurements.

> **Key knowledge:** To find the lengths of unknown sides of a shape, think about any measurements you already know and use the properties of shapes to help you.

Free Running

Within *Free Running*, children are presented with two possible designs for a rope perimeter. They are also given the total length of rope that can be used and the dimensions of the M-PODS that must be enclosed within it. They must draw a possible plan for each design.

In *S.I.D.'s Challenge*, what appears to be a more complicated design is introduced. Again, the children must come up with possible dimensions and then consider whether there was an easier method to calculate the perimeter.

Sharing Results and Evaluating

Look for children who use a method of multiplication rather than repeated addition.

Spend time exploring different shapes and measuring perimeters. Look for more irregular shapes where calculating the perimeter seems more complex, but as for *S.I.D.'s Challenge*, translation of sides can form a more straightforward shape.

Answers
Starting Off

1. 23.4 m
   7.8 m × 3 (or 7.8 + 7.8 + 7.8)
2. 2922 cm (29.22 m)
   (2 × 836) + (2 x 625) or 2 × (836 + 625)

Away We Go

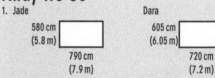

1. Jade / Dara

2. Jade 27.4 m (2740 cm)
   Dara 26.5 m (2650 cm)
3. 10.8 m (1080 cm)
4. No, because the total perimeter is 45.95 m (4595 cm) and this is 95 cm longer than the rope they have.

Free Running

1. Possible solutions include:

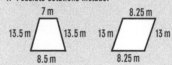

NB width must accommodate Jade's M-POD and length must be at least 12 m (5.6 m + 6.4 m) for both pods.

S.I.D.'s Challenge

In the solution check that the two measurements (e.g. 7 m + 1 m shown here) add to the length of the base (e.g. 8 m here) and the same is true for the other sides (e.g. 6.5 + 6.5 and 13 m). A quicker way is e.g. 2 x (8 + 13) for the reasons explained above.

THE MISSION IN CRISIS
Solving problems about place value.

> The arguments between the Mariners have now come to a head and the pairs are planning their next steps.

△ Starting Off

LII	LXXII	LVI	LXXII

XII	LVI	XXIV	XLVIII	XII	LXXX	LXXVI

XXXII	XLVIII	LXIV

Jade, we should let Irina know what is going on. I'm worried that our feuds may be a threat to the mission if they continue. We could send her a message in code …

Jade and Dara decide to send their message as Roman numerals; they know that Zack and Ceri are not very good at understanding them.
But just in case, they decide to leave out all vowels!

1. Write the numbers that the Roman numerals represent.

2. What is the message sent to Earth Control? The code is A = 4, B = 8, C = 12, etc.

3. Write the Roman numerals for all the missing vowels.

◁ Away We Go

Meanwhile, Zack and Ceri are making their own plans …

Perhaps we can change some of the data that the others have given to S.I.D.

That's a great idea; then it looks like we are leading this mission …

They decide to change the values of the readings Dara and Jade have taken from the coolant controls on the M-PODs so that their own readings appear **higher**.

A	2	3	4	5	6
B	2	3	4	5	6
C	5	8	1	5	3
D	4	9	0	4	5
E	1	5	9	8	7

1. What is the value of the digit **5** in all of these numbers?
2. How many times smaller is the value of the digit **8** in reading E than in reading C?
3. Ceri decides to swap around the digits **3** and **4** in reading B.
   Why is this not a good idea?

Zack decides that the best idea is to change all the digits in reading C so that it reads **44444**.

A	2	9	4	5	1
B	3	4	5	6	7
C	5	8	1	5	3
D	4	9	0	1	5
E	1	5	9	8	7

He has to type in the place value of the digit he wants to add or subtract each time.

4. What will Zack have to type into the computer?

> **HINT:** For example, to change the digit **5** in the number 57 to a **3**, type in −20 (subtract 20)

5. Ceri decides to do the same to one of the other readings so it will read **33333**

She types in

−6000	−2	−10000	+300	+20

Which reading did she change in this way?

Free Running

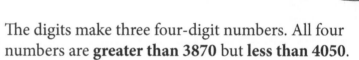

Attention, Mariners! Someone has been tampering with my computer …

S.I.D.'s screen begins to scramble as single digits fly all over the place …

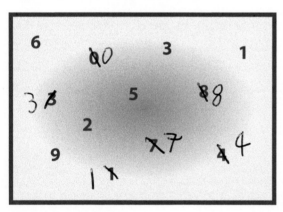

The digits make three four-digit numbers. All four numbers are **greater than 3870** but **less than 4050**.

1. What could the three numbers be?
 Write your solutions in order from smallest to largest.

2. Now find another possible solution.

S.I.D.'s Challenge

Value of symbol	1000	100	10	1
Number of symbols	10	17	13	9

The three four-digit number can be represented using the symbols shown.
e.g. 132 is shown as

The table shows how many each symbol was used in the three numbers.

What could the three numbers be now? Check to see whether any of your solutions still work.

THE MISSION IN CRISIS

TEACHER'S NOTES

Curriculum Focus

1. Recognise the place value of each digit in a four-digit number (extending to five digits).
2. Order and compare numbers beyond 1000.
3. Identify, represent and estimate numbers using different representations.
4. Read Roman numerals to 100 (I to C).

Running the Activity

Background

Are the children secure with their understanding of place value for four-digit numbers? Can they also apply this understanding to five-digit numbers?

How familiar are they with Roman numerals up to 100? Do they understand how, over time, the numeral system changed to include the concept of zero and place value?

Are they secure when multiplying numbers by 10, 100 and 1000 and can they explain the effect?

These tasks require children to use their knowledge of place value to make decisions about the size of numbers and their relative position to each other.

Starting Off

Within *Starting Off*, children use their knowledge of Roman numerals to 100 to help crack a code. They must also write the numbers 4, 20, 36, 60 and 84 in Roman numerals.

> **Key knowledge:** In Roman numerals, numbers from 1 to 100 can be made using combinations of I, V, X and L only.

Away We Go

Within *Away We Go*, children move on to consider the value of digits in five-digit numbers and compare values when they appear in different positions in the number. Children must then use the value of each digit to help them make decisions about how to change them in the context of the problem.

> **Key knowledge:** We need to know the value of each digit in a number so that we know how large or small it is and how it compares to other numbers.

Free Running

Within *Free Running*, children are required to create three four-digit numbers that are greater than 3870 but less than 4050. They will need to make decisions about the position of the digits to create the most significant values, i.e. thousands and hundreds in this case.

In *S.I.D.'s Challenge*, children must interpret symbols that represent 1, 10, 100 and 1000 and use the criteria given to find a solution that still fits.

Sharing Results and Evaluating

Look for children who confidently explain the value of digits in larger numbers and use this knowledge to help order the numbers.

Look for children who recognise how single digit numbers are written in Roman numerals and apply this to larger numbers, i.e. using 9 (IX) to help write 29 (XIX).

Share solutions and reasoning for *Free Running* and look for further possibilities.

Answers

Starting Off

1.

LII	LXXII	LVI	LXXII
52	72	56	72

XII	LVI	XXIV	XLVIII	XII	LXXX	LXXVI
12	56	24	48	12	80	76

XXXII	XLVIII	LXIV
32	48	64

2. MRNR   CNFLCTS   HLP
3. A = IV, E = XX, I = XXXVI, O = LX, U = LXXXIV

Away We Go

1. A (50), B (500), C (50,000 and 50), D (5), E (5000)
2. 100 times smaller
3. This would make the number larger and they want to make them smaller.
4.

5	8	1	5	3
−10,000	−4000	+300	−10	+1

5. Reading D

Free Running

1. and 2. Solutions include: 3871, 3952, 4016
3875, 3960, 4021

S.I.D.'s Challenge

Possible solutions are: 3872, 3951, 4016, or 3871, 3952, 4016 or 3872, 3956, 4011 or 3876, 3952, 4016 etc.
NB One number must be 387_ and another 401_ so that they are still all greater than 3870 and less than 4050.

MAKING UP
Solving problems about area.

➤ The Mariners have been talking about a truce and how they can repair their relationships after all the troubles that they have had recently.

◬ Starting Off

They begin by discussing all the areas they have 'roped-off' at Base camp and how this has caused a real problem between them all.

> Well, you two had a larger area in the **Gym**!

4.2 m

3 m | **Zack and Ceri**

2.7 m

5 m | **Jade and Dara**

HINT: We use **m²** to represent **square metres**, e.g. 2 m² or 2 square metres can be shown as where the length of each side of a square is 1 m.

1. Who could the Mystery Mariner be? Explain how you know.
2. How much smaller is their area of the **Gym**? Show your answer as ___ m².

◁ Away We Go

> Attention, Mariners! I have noticed that each pair sometimes has the larger area!

S.I.D. shows the Mariners all the 'roped-off' areas at Base camp.

	Kitchen	Growing M-POD	Working space	Relaxing space
Jade and Dara	21 m²	48 m²	50.5 m²	28 m²
Zack and Ceri	24 m²	36 m²	60.6 m²	27 m²

1. Which pair of Mariners has the greatest area in total here?
2. How many more square metres (m²) do they have? Explain how you know. *'I know … because …'*
3.

7 m

4 m

These are the dimensions of one of the areas from the table above. Which area is this and who did it belong to?

The Mariners go off to measure all of their areas that were on the table that S.I.D. had shown them. They record their measurements like this:

I'm not sure all of that information is correct, S.I.D.

? cm

Zack and Ceri
Kitchen

? cm

24 m²

780 cm

HINT: Think about the number facts you know and how they can help you.

4. Record all the areas in the same way and find out possible values each side of the rectangular areas.

5. Can you find some areas that could have been made in more than one way? Show some different possibilities.

▷ Free Running

The Mariners are still not happy, especially when someone mentions the way that their outside space has been 'roped-off'!

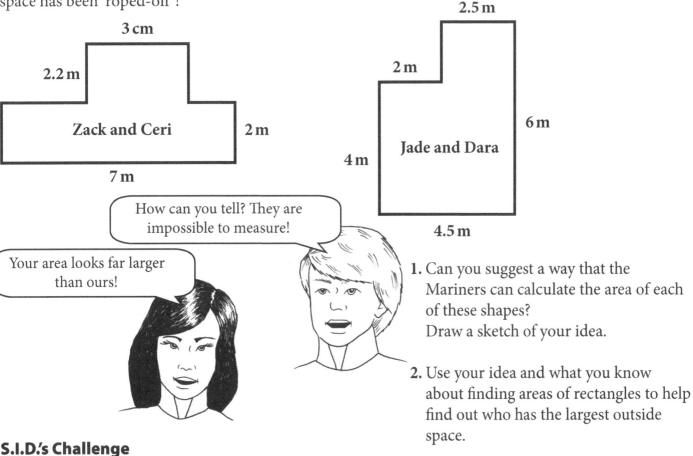

3 cm

2.2 m

Zack and Ceri

2 m

7 m

2.5 m

2 m

6 m

Jade and Dara

4 m

4.5 m

How can you tell? They are impossible to measure!

Your area looks far larger than ours!

1. Can you suggest a way that the Mariners can calculate the area of each of these shapes?
   Draw a sketch of your idea.

2. Use your idea and what you know about finding areas of rectangles to help find out who has the largest outside space.

S.I.D.'s Challenge

After discovering that there were times when neither pair has been very fair, they decide that they really should bring their quarrels to an end.

They remove all of the ropes from the gym, outdoor space, kitchen, working space and relaxing space.

1. Using all the information you have, calculate the total areas for each of these.

2. Order the areas from largest to smallest.

MAKING UP

TEACHER'S NOTES

Curriculum Focus

1. Find the area of rectilinear shapes by counting and relating area to arrays and multiplication.
2. Recognise and use factor pairs and commutativity in mental calculations.
3. Recall multiplication and division facts for multiplication tables up to 12×12.

Running the Activity
Background

What experience do the children have of counting squares or half squares to find the area of shapes?

Are they secure with the knowledge that arrays can be used to represent numbers and the dimensions of the array are factors of the number it represents? Also, do they recognise that a number may have more than one array?

Have they experienced calculating area using the relationship to the array and understand the link to multiplication? Do they understand how units of measurement are used to describe area?

These tasks require children to draw on knowledge of measurement, factors and multiples and begin to think about areas of compound shapes.

Starting Off

Within *Starting Off*, children are given the dimensions of two areas and must prove which one is the largest.

> *Key knowledge:* We use m² to represent square metres, e.g. 2 m² or 2 square metres can be shown as ☐☐ where the length of each side of a square is 1 m.

Away We Go

Within *Away We Go*, children move on to comparing areas given and recognising possible dimensions that would result in this area. As the problem extends, they must draw on knowledge of factors and multiples.

> *Key knowledge:* The area of a rectangle can also be shown as an array, where the dimensions of the array (rectangle) are factors of the number (area) it represents.

Free Running

Within *Free Running*, children will work with compound shapes made up of two different rectangles. They must find the dimensions of each using the measurements shown.

S.I.D.'s Challenge requires the children to total all areas and then order them from largest to smallest.

Sharing Results and Evaluating

Look for children who confidently relate area to arrays and multiplication and draw on these facts accordingly. Share possible dimensions for areas that can be made in more than one way and relate this to arrays. Begin to explore other compound shapes using knowledge of the area of rectangles.

Answers
Starting Off
1. Zack or Ceri because the area of their section of the Gym is only 12.6 m² and the others have 13.5 m².
2. Their area is 0.9 m² smaller.

Away We Go
1. Zack and Ceri
2. 0.1 m² 'I know because Zack and Ceri had 147.6 m² altogether and Jade and Dara only had 147.5 m² which is 0.1 m² less.'
3. Relaxing space for Jade and Dara 28 m²
4. Example solutions include:
   Kitchen (J&D 7 m × 3 m) (Z&C 4 m × 6 m)
   Growing M-POD (J&D 6 m × 8 m) (Z&C 6 m × 6 m)
   Working space (J&D 5 m × 10.1 m) (Z&C 6 m × 10.1 m)
   Relaxing space (J&D 4 m × 7 m) (Z&C 3 m × 7 m)
5. Using factors to help, other examples would include:
   24 m² (3 m × 8 m; 2 m × 12 m, etc.)
   48 m² (4 m × 12 m; 2 m × 24 m, etc.)
   36 m² (3 m × 12 m; 9 m × 4 m; 2 m ×18 m, etc.)
   etc.

Free Running
1. Split the shape up into rectangles, e.g.

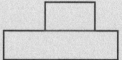

2. Zack and Ceri's outside space can be split into a 3 m × 2.2 m rectangle and a 2 m × 7 m rectangle giving a total area of 20.6 m².

   Jade and Dara's outside space can be split into a 2.5 m × 6 m rectangle and a 2 m × 4 m rectangle, giving a total area of 23 m².

   Jade and Dara have the largest outside space.

S.I.D.'s Challenge
1. and 2. Largest to smallest:
working space 111.1 m², growing M-POD 84 m², relaxing space 55 m², kitchen 54 m², outside space 43.6 m², gym 26.1 m²

AN M-POD MAKEOVER
Solving problems about factors and multiples.

➤ After all the recent conflict, the Mariners decide to make some improvements to their home and make the Base larger.

△ Starting Off

Zack suggests that all outside areas should be made seven times larger.

> Attention, Mariners! Let's begin by making parts of the Base larger.

	Area 1	Area 2	Area 3	Area 4
Original	12 m²		15 m²	
7 times larger		147 m²		84 m²

1. Copy and complete the table.

2. Write the calculations that you needed to use to find the original size of Area 2 and Area 4.

3. Zack also decided they should make **Area 5** seven times larger.
   He wrote that the original area is a **whole m²**. The enlarged area is **100 m²**.
   Jade knew that Zack had made a mistake without even calculating.
   How did she know? *'Jade knew Zack had made a mistake because …'*

◁ Away We Go

Ceri calculates how many more plants they could grow if they built another growing M-POD.

> That's a great idea, Zack, but how about the growing M-POD?
> I think that we should be able to grow more plants now. Perhaps we need another M-POD?

Broccoli	**Onions**	**Tomatoes**
72 more	120 more	? more

The plants will all be arranged in **equal rows**.
1. How many different ways can they arrange the broccoli plants in equal rows?
2. How many different ways can they arrange the onions in equal rows?
3. Is it possible to arrange the broccoli or onions in equal rows of seven? Explain your thinking.

4. Is it possible to arrange the onions in an odd number of rows with an odd number of plants in each row?

'It is possible because …' or *'It is not possible because …'*

Ceri would like to be able to arrange the number of tomato plants in equal rows of eight **or** in equal rows of nine.

5. Investigate to find out how many more tomato plants Ceri can have in total. Present your findings in a table.

> **HINT:** Think carefully about the labels you will use for your table.

Free Running

The Mariners are very keen to make other improvements and each go off to decide what they would like to do.

> I think that we should think about some other improvements that we would like.

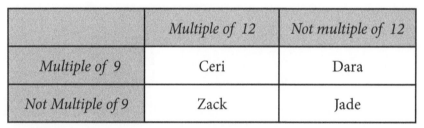

	Multiple of 12	Not multiple of 12
Multiple of 9	Ceri	Dara
Not Multiple of 9	Zack	Jade

They all decide that they would like more specimen jars to take out on their adventures. Everyone asked for **more than 30** specimen jars.

1. Use the information from the Carroll diagram to suggest some possible numbers of specimen jars requested by each Mariner.
Find at least three possibilities for each **Mariner**.

2. Is it possible for Ceri and Zack to ask for the same number of jars?
Explain your thinking.

S.I.D.'s Challenge

The Mariners ask S.I.D. for a **multiple of 100** more specimen jars.
Find a solution to the problem now using what you have found out from the previous task to help you.

> **HINT:** Remember that everyone asked for more than 30 specimen jars.

AN M-POD MAKEOVER

TEACHER'S NOTES

Curriculum Focus

1. Count in multiples of 6, 7, 9, 25 and 1000.
2. Recognise and use factor pairs and commutativity in mental calculations.
3. Recall multiplication and division facts for multiplication tables up to 12×12.

Running the Activity
Background

How regularly do children reason about the properties of numbers and the relationships between them? Is it common place for the children to use the language of factors and multiples when describing these relationships?

Do they confidently draw on knowledge of the multiplication and division facts and use these, and partitioning, to help make decisions about numbers that go beyond the twelfth multiple?

These tasks require children to draw upon knowledge of factors and multiples to solve problems.

Starting Off

Within *Starting Off*, children use multiplication and division facts related to the seven times tables. The numbers concerned all relate to the twelfth or beyond the twelfth multiple.

> *Key knowledge:* When numbers to be divided go beyond known facts, partitioning is a useful strategy to split the number into parts where known facts (and place value) can be more easily applied.

Away We Go

Within *Away We Go*, children move on to solve problems relating to factors where more than one pair of factors needs to be found. They will also need to reason about the result of multiplying two odd numbers together.

The problem extends to consider common multiples and children will have to decide how the solutions can be arranged in a table.

> *Key knowledge:* The product of two odd numbers will always be odd. An even number will either have pairs of factors where both are even or where one is even and the other is odd.

Free Running

Within *Free Running*, children are shown a set of criteria presented in a Carroll Diagram. They must use this information to explore possible values for each Mariner, including finding common multiples of nine and twelve.

S.I.D.'s Challenge presents an additional criterion that needs to be suited to find a possible solution to the original problem. With a total that is a multiple of 100, the children will need to remember to look either for numbers that are all even or to include a pair of odd numbers.

Sharing Results and Evaluating

Look for children who use partitioning effectively to support them to find factors of given numbers.
Look for those who recognise the commutativity of pairs of factors, e.g. 7×8 and 8×7.
Share solutions for the Carroll diagram problem and particularly look at children's explanations for question 2.

Answers
Starting Off

1.

	Area 1	Area 2	Area 3	Area 4
Original	12 m²	21 m²	15 m²	12 m²
7 times larger	84 m²	147 m²	105 m²	84 m²

2. $147 \div 7$ and $84 \div 7$
3. 'Jade knew Zack had made a mistake because 100 is not a multiple of seven.'

Away We Go

1. 1 row of 72 or 72 rows of 1
   2 rows of 36 or 36 rows of 2
   3 rows of 24 or 24 rows of 3
   4 rows of 18 or 18 rows of 4
   6 rows of 12 or 12 rows of 6
   8 rows of 9 or 9 rows of 8
2. 1 row of 120 or 120 rows of 1
   2 rows of 60 or 60 rows of 2
   3 rows of 40 or 40 rows of 3
   4 rows of 30 or 30 rows of 4
   5 rows of 24 or 24 rows of 5
   6 rows of 20 or 20 rows of 6
   8 rows of 15 or 15 rows of 8
   10 rows of 12 or 12 rows of 10
3. No, because neither are multiples of seven.
4. E.g. 'It is not possible because the product of two odd numbers is always odd and 120 is even.'
5. Common multiples of 8 and 9, e.g. 72 and 144, etc.

Free Running

1. Ceri (e.g. 36, 72, 108) Dara (e.g. 45, 54, 63)
   Zack (e.g. 48, 60, 84) Jade (e.g. 31, 32, 33)
2. No, because if it were the same number they would be in the same set together.

S.I.D.'s Challenge
Children's own examples.
E.g. Ceri 36, Dara 54, Zack 60, Jade 50 (total 200)
    Ceri 72, Dara 45, Zack 48, Jade 35 (total 200), etc.

REPAIRING THE ROVER
Solving problems about angles.

➤ There seems to be a problem with the Rover.

◭ Starting Off

The Mariners are setting off on another adventure, but there seems to be something wrong with the Rover …

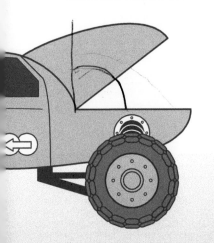

Dara lifts up the bonnet to check the engine. The bonnet turns through an angle as it opens.

HINT: Angles can be described acute, right angle, obtuse straight or reflex.

1. What is the name of the angle shown here?

2. Estimate the angle shown and explain your decision.

'I think that the angle is approximately … degrees because …'

3. The maximum angle that the bonnet can turn through is $\frac{9}{10}$ of a right angle. What angle is this?

◁ Away We Go

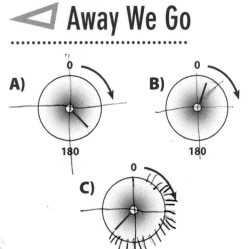

A)

B)

C)

I just need to check that the three fuel controls are working first …

1. Estimate the angle that each of these controls has turned from z•

2. Order the angles from smallest to largest and name each one.

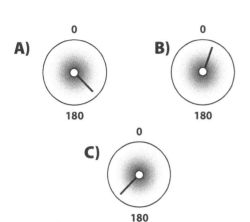

A) 0 / 180

B) 0 / 180

C) 0 / 180

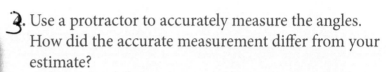

Oh, we have a problem, guys. The fuel controls are not in the correct position.

All controls should be at **180°**.

3. Use a protractor to accurately measure the angles. How did the accurate measurement differ from your estimate?

4. Through what angle must Dara turn the controls so that they are all at 180°?

HINT: Remember to say whether the turn is clockwise or anti-clockwise.

▷Free Running

Mariners, you may want to check that the air pressure controls are also in the correct position.

Control A   Control B   Control C

All controls show an angle that is a multiple of 5°.

Control A + Control B = 180°
Control C > 180°
Control B < right angle
Control C − Control B = 130°

1. Use the information here to find all possible values for Control A, Control B and Control C. Decide how you are going to show your findings.

2. Explain why Control B cannot be at 50°.
'Control B cannot be at 50° because …'

S.I.D.'s Challenge

Dara turns all controls on the air pressure display back to the correct position of **160°** and the Rover roars into life again. All the turns he makes are **acute** and are all **multiples of 10°**. One of the turns is anti-clockwise.

Which original positions for Controls A, B and C from your previous investigation are still possible? Find a way to prove how you know.

REPAIRING THE ROVER

TEACHER'S NOTES

Curriculum Focus

Identify acute and obtuse angles and compare and order angles up to two right angles by size.

Running the Activity

Background

What experience do the children have of controlling classroom 'robots'? Have they used knowledge of fractions of turns to help make decisions when giving instructions?

Do the children recognise that a quarter turn is equivalent to a right-angle turn and this is measured as 90°?

Have the children practised using a set square or protractor to determine whether an angle is greater or less than 90°? Do they confidently use the language associated with angles and correctly name and explain why an angle is acute, right angle or obtuse?

These tasks require children to name, estimate and measure angles, making decisions about necessary turns that need to be made to solve problems.

◢ Starting Off

Within *Starting Off*, children estimate and name an acute angle. They must also explain why the angle is acute and use knowledge of fractions, and what they know about the number of degrees in a right angle, to find an unknown angle.

> *Key knowledge:* Acute angles measure less than 90°, which is less than a quarter of a full turn.

◁ Away We Go

Within *Away We Go*, children move on to estimate, name and order three different angles including acute, obtuse and reflex.
The problem extends to deciding the turns that need to be made to return each dial to a 180° position.

> *Key knowledge:* It is important to know the direction of a turn. *Clockwise* is the direction that the hands turn on a clock whilst anti-clockwise is the opposite direction.

▷ Free Running

Within *Free Running*, children are presented with a set of related facts and equations that are to be used to find possible values for each control.
They must find a way to record their findings.

In *S.I.D.'s Challenge*, some additional information is provided relating to the amount of turn needed to correct each of the controls. Children must decide which of their previous solutions are still possible.

Sharing Results and Evaluating

Look for children who use knowledge of a quarter or half turn to make estimates about the size of angles.
Look for children who describe angles accurately using the language of acute, obtuse, etc. and can explain the properties they each have.
Share solutions from *Free Running* and look at pairs of angles that total 180° establishing that these make a straight angle, i.e. angles at a point on a straight line.

Answers

Starting Off

1. Acute
   'I think that the angle is approximately 45° because it is about half of a right angle.'
2. 81°

Away We Go

1. Control A: estimate between 130° and 140°
   Control B: estimate between 20° and 30°
   Control C: estimate between 225° and 240°
2. 20° (acute), 135° (obtuse), 235° (reflex)
3. Control A 135°, Control B 20° and Control C 225°
   Children's own comparisons to estimates.
4. Control A, turn of 45° clockwise
   Control B, turn of 160° clockwise
   Control C, turn of 55° anti-clockwise

Free Running

1. These are all possible solutions

A	B	C
95°	85°	215°
100°	80°	210°
105°	75°	205°
110°	70°	200°
115°	65°	195°
120°	60°	190°
125°	55°	185°

2. Control B cannot be at 50°, because this would make Control C 170° and we know it is larger than 180°.

S.I.D.'s Challenge

Only one solution is still possible as all others would not be a turn that is a multiple of 10° or where Control B is also acute:

Control A	Control B	Control C
100° (60° CW)	80° (80° CW)	210° (50° ACW)

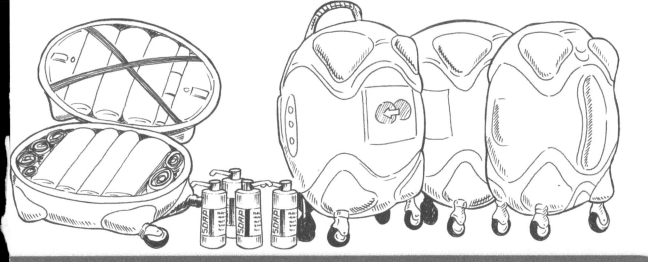

WORKING WITH *CURIOSITY*
Solving problems about using multiplication and division facts.

➤ The Mariners decide to give some of their samples to *Curiosity* to analyse for scientists back on Earth. They are waiting for the results.

Starting Off

ROCK   PAPER   SCISSORS

To pass the time, the Mariners begin to play their version of the 'rock-paper-scissors' game.

Rules
- Players choose the multiplication that each hand signal will represent, e.g. rocks = ×2.
- 1st player chooses a starting number between 0 and 12.
- On the count of three, the 2nd and 3rd players show the hand signal for rock, paper or scissors.
- The 4th player must shout the answer to the calculation before their team mates.

The Mariners decide that ...
ROCK = × 10   PAPER = × 6   SCISSORS = × 8
The table shows the first three games.

1. What answer should the 4th player shout each time?

2. Ceri thinks that using the SCISSORS before the ROCK in the first game will give a different answer. What do you think?

Start number	Hand signals	Answer
7	✊ ✌️	
5	✌️ ✌️	
11	✋ ✊	

Away We Go

In the next game, ROCK = × 9 PAPER = × 100 SCISSORS = × 4

1. Using Jade's starting number, find all the possible answers that Dara should shout.

*Are you ready, Dara? I choose **three** as the starting number!*

HINT: Decide which number it would be more useful to multiply by first.

Here are the results of the next four games of 'rock-paper-scissors'.

ROCK = × 9   PAPER = × 100   SCISSORS = × 4

2. Copy and complete the table.

> **HINT:** Write **R** for ROCK,
>   **S** for SCISSORS and
>   **P** for PAPER.

Start number	Hand signals	Answer
?		8100
5	 ?	180
?		81
7	 ?	2800

▷ Free Running

LIZARD

Hey, guys, let's make things more interesting! Let's add a fourth hand signal and let's make three hand signals each time! We can even use division …

8   6   12

Starting numbers

ROCK = × 10   PAPER = × 5   SCISSORS = × 3   LIZARD = ÷ 2

1. Choose one of the starting numbers each time and find as many answers as you can using three hand signals.

  e.g.   **Start 8   R, P, L = 200**

2. Does the order still **not** matter when division is included?
3. Why would this game be rather boring if **ROCK = × 0**?
  'It would be rather boring because …'

S.I.D.'s Challenge

Curiosity analysed **720 samples in total**. Samples are arranged in **equal** rows in a tray.

Investigate the different ways the samples can be arranged in a tray and how many trays are needed each time.

Find a way to show what you have found out.

Trays of samples

WORKING WITH *CURIOSITY*

TEACHER'S NOTES

Curriculum Focus

1. Recall multiplication and division facts for multiplication tables up to 12 × 12.
2. Use place value, known and derived facts to multiply and divide mentally, including: multiplying by 0 and 1; dividing by 1; multiplying together three numbers.

Running the Activity
Background

What experience do the children have of multiplying more than two numbers together?

How confidently can they explain that multiplication is commutative so the answer will be the same when calculated in any order?

Do they recognise that when one of the operators is × 10 or × 100, etc. it is often easier to do this last? e.g. 9 × 10 × 7 may be easier as 9 × 7 × 10 so that two single digits can be multiplied first, however this may not be the case when decimals are involved.

Do children confidently apply division as the inverse of multiplication so that they can 'undo' a calculation?

These tasks require children to multiply three and then four numbers together (one of which is always a multiple of ten) and make decisions about the most efficient order in which to calculate.

Starting Off

Within *Starting Off*, children are introduced to the Mariners' version of a game. They are required to give the product of three numbers and explain why the order of the calculation does not matter.

> *Key knowledge:* Multiplication, like addition, is commutative, which means it can be done in any order and the result remains the same.

Away We Go

Within *Away We Go*, children move on to investigating the combinations of hand signals, and therefore, calculations. The problem extends to using the results of several games and applying the inverse to identify starting numbers or operators.

> *Key knowledge:* When multiplying or dividing by 4, it is useful to factorise, using x 2 x 2 or ÷ 2 ÷ 2

Free Running

Within *Free Running*, children are given a fourth hand signal of division. Again, they must investigate different combinations, and consider whether division has an effect on the order of the calculation.

In *S.I.D.'s Challenge* they apply the skills of multiplying three numbers together to help find different solutions to a problem involving the samples. They will need to consider factors of 720 to help them.

Sharing Results and Evaluating

Look for children who can confidently explain that the multiplication of any string of numbers can be done in any order and that this is the same when division is included, e.g. 7 × 4 ÷ 2 = 7 ÷ 2 × 4.
Look for children who recognise when to apply the inverse to help 'undo' a calculation.

Share solutions for the four hand signals and then challenge children to decide on their own values for the symbols and play the game.

Answers
Starting Off
1. 560, 320, 660
2. 7 × 10 × 8 will give the same results as 7 × 8 × 10

Away We Go
1. Starting number is three so:

R, R 3 × 9 x 9 = 243	S, S 3 × 4 × 4 = 48
P, P 3 × 100 x 100 = 30000	R, S 3 × 9 × 4 = 108
R, P 3 × 9 x 100 = 2700	P, S 3 × 100 × 4 = 1200

2.

Start number	Hand signals	Answer
9	R P	8100
5	S R	180
1	R R	81
7	S P	2800

Free Running
1. Children's own investigations, e.g.
   12 L L L = 1.5 12 R R R = 12000
   6 R S L = 90, etc.
2. The calculation can be done in any order and the answer is the same.
3. 'It would be rather boring because when you multiply by zero the answer is always zero.'

S.I.D.'s Challenge
10 trays: 1 × 72 or 2 × 36 or 3 × 24, etc.
1 tray: 72 × 10 or 720 × 1 or 5 x 144, etc.
2 trays: 1 × 360 or 10 × 36 or 20 × 18 or 6 × 60
3 trays: 1 × 240 or 10 × 24, etc.

A BRIEF ENCOUNTER ...
Solving problems about coordinates.

➤ The Mariners are fast asleep, but a sudden flash of bright light wakes them from their slumber.

◮ Starting Off

What on Mars is that?!

Dara is the first to race to the main control panels in the M-PODS.
He needs to find out what is going on …

Three points are flashing on the radar display.

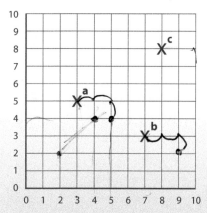

On the display panel, the coordinates of the three points **a**, **b** and **c** are shown.

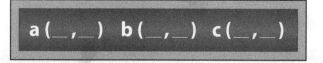

a (_ , _)   b (_ , _)   c (_ , _)

1. Write the coordinates for points **a**, **b** and **c**.

2. Suddenly the flashing points all move **two squares** to the **right** and **one square down**. Write their new coordinates.

◁ Away We Go

*Dara, what's going on?
What can you see?*

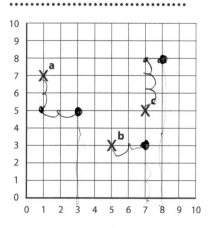

Dara shows Ceri the flashing points on the radar, but they have moved again!

1. Compare the new positions of **a**, **b** and **c** with the first ones that Dara shown on the grid above. Describe how each point has moved.

> **HINT:** Use the vocabulary left, right, up or do to help you. Remember to say how ma squares they move each time.

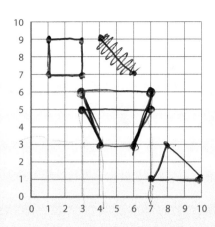

2. Use a 10 by 10 grid like this. With a ruler, carefully draw each of these three shapes on the grid.
Give the coordinates for each shape.

HINT: Remember that the square is a regular shape.

▷ Free Running

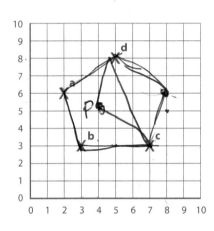

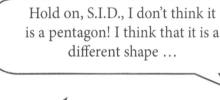

Attention, Mariners, attention! You need to all come immediately! I am unable to explain what this is, but it seems to be in the shape of an unidentified flying object … a UFO!

There is one point missing from the shape on the radar.
S.I.D. thinks that the 'UFO' is in the shape of a pentagon.
1. What is the missing coordinate?

Hold on, S.I.D., I don't think it is a pentagon! I think that it is a different shape …

2. Jade sketches the new shape.
Is the shape still a pentagon?
What is the missing coordinate now?
Label this point **p**.

S.I.D.'s Challenge

The 'UFO' seems to be getting closer and it makes a half turn …
Point **d** moves to the coordinate (5 , 3)
Draw the new position of the 'UFO' and write the coordinates of all the points.

You don't suppose …
… it could be ALIENS?!

AN AMAZING PLACE

Think of the amazing places you have been discussing in class, such as giant caves, mountains, canyons, deserts and icebergs.

Imagine you are visiting one of these amazing places for the first time. How do you feel? What kinds of sounds can you hear? What sights can you see?

Write down some powerful adjectives to describe this place.

_____

_____

_____

_____

Now turn the words about the place you have chosen into a poem.

TEACHER'S NOTES

Introduction

- Load up the Mind's Eye CD-ROM. You may like to tell the children what the title of the session is before you reveal the image, or just open up the picture and watch their initial reactions to it.

- With the whole image in view, invite the children to share their first impressions of the image. Establish that it is a young boy gazing out of a window.

Familiarisation

- Look closely at the image together and discuss why the boy's face seems blurred. Where might such a patterned window be located? Would it be a home rather than a school or other building? Could it be a bathroom or front door window? Are there leaves in the pattern on the glass? Are there drops of water on the glass, suggesting rain?

- How old do the children think this boy may be? Can we tell from looking closely at his face what sort of mood he is in? Is he happy/sad? Is he waiting for someone, e.g. the postman? Why?

Exploration

- Invite the children to explore captions in the form of single words or short phrases that could be written beneath this image to sum up what is going on in the picture. You may wish to brainstorm these on the board using a mind-map.

- Ask the children to pretend that the boy is waiting for someone or something. Ask them to suggest what this could be, e.g. postman on his birthday, his father to come home from work, the rain to stop.

Boy standing behind glass door.
© Joel Sartoe/National Geographic/Getty Images

ACTIVITIES

Speaking

- **Thought tracking:** Working in pairs, one partner assumes the role of the little boy (or it could be a girl) at the window. The other person must express the thoughts that might be going through his/her head, based on their body language and facial expression.

Listening

- **Hot seating:** Invite volunteers to take turns sitting in the 'hot seat' at the front of the class and answer questions in the role of the little boy in the picture. Each time a different person plays the game they must try to offer different reasons for staring out of the window.

 Group Discussion

- **Class discussion:** Begin a discussion about how we feel on wet days at home, when we cannot go outside to play or visit friends. Invite the children to share ideas about how to amuse themselves and discuss what they do at home on a rainy day.

- **Group discussion:** In groups of about three or four, make a list (on large paper) of exciting activities to break the boredom of rainy days at home. Use the ideas referred to in the class discussion above, and other new and imaginative ideas.

Drama

- **Paired role-play:** Ask the children to get into pairs for this exercise. One partner plays the part of the boy in the picture. He is waiting and waiting for something special to arrive (e.g. birthday cards, competition prize, toy). The other partner plays the part of the delivery person/postman. Encourage the children to show the contrast between the boy's feelings before and after the delivery.

Extension

- **Group drama:** In groups, complete the following scene. The little boy is actually outside a toy shop, staring in at his favourite toy. He knows he can never have it because his parents cannot afford it. One day he notices thieves in the shop… Complete the story together.

DEAR DIARY...

Have you ever felt bored in the middle of a long summer holiday? The boy in the picture has played with all his toys and games and can't think of anything else to do.

Look closely at the picture again and try to climb inside the boy's mind. Imagine how he is feeling today, then write down a short diary entry to describe his dull day and how he cheers himself up.

_____

_____

_____

_____

_____

_____

_____

_____

_____

_____

_____

Practise reading your diary piece aloud and then share it with your class.

TEACHER'S NOTES

Introduction

- Load up the Mind's Eye CD-ROM. You may like to tell the children what the title of the session is before you reveal the image, or just open up the picture and watch their initial reactions to it.

- With the whole image in view, invite the children to offer suggestions about what is happening here. What has caught fire? Where? How?

Familiarisation

- Discuss the children's prior knowledge and experience of fires in natural environments such as forests, heath land etc. How do they start? What enables them to spread so quickly? Discuss dry conditions, sun, wind. How can fires be extinguished? Talk about hose pipes, pumps, helicopters.

- Can the children remember hearing about any fires of this kind in news reports? Where do these sorts of fires often occur, and why? Think particularly about Australia with its dry conditions and very hot, strong winds.

Exploration

- Have the children heard of the practice of burning off stubble on farms? Do they know why this happens?

- Invite the children to think about other sorts of fires a firefighter like this might have to attend. Which might be the worst or the most dangerous (e.g. chemical fires, oil rigs)?

Firefighter tackling heather moorland blaze, Brecon Beacons National Park, South Wales. © *Jeff Morgan/Alamy*

ACTIVITIES

👄 Speaking

- **Personal thoughts:** Ask the children to consider if they would like to be a firefighter or not. Invite them to share with the group their response giving reasons for their comments.

- **Hot seating:** Invite volunteers to take turns sitting in the 'hot seat' at the front of the class and answer questions in the role of the firefighter in the picture. Questions could include: *How quickly did you get to the fire? How do you think it was started? How did it feel being so close to the flames? Why did you become a firefighter?*

👂 Listening

- **Note taking:** Explain to the group that they will need to use their listening skills to make notes during the class discussion about the dangerous occupations that are mentioned and what their risks are. You may wish to assess how well they have listened by checking their notes.

👁 Group Discussion

- **Class discussion:** Initiate a discussion on occupations that involve great risk. Invite the children to share their ideas and discuss why certain jobs are dangerous. Would any of the children like to take on one of these jobs when they are older? Why? Examples could include police officer, soldier, stunt man/woman, bomb disposal expert, mountain rescue officer, coastguard.

🎭 Drama

- **Group drama:** Invite the children to work in groups of about three or four. The scenario for the role-play is that they are a group of friends walking through a forest together. Gradually they become aware of a burning smell and they then see smoke and flames in the distance. A forest fire has started and they need to find help quickly. How will they complete this scene?

- **TV advertisement:** Discuss with the children how fires can be started accidentally. Their task is to prepare a two minute television advertisement/public service broadcast that warns people of the dangers of causing fires through discarding cigarettes, lighting their own fires and misusing camping stoves and candles.

❗ Extension

- **Paired work:** In pairs, ask the children to identify the qualities one might need to become a firefighter. Record answers on the board in a final plenary (examples include: *courage, strength, physical fitness, agility, compassion, a level head, calm in a crisis*). Explore inventions/developments that might change the role of firefighters in the future.

FLICKERING MONSTERS

Look again at the fire in the picture. Think about the red and orange flames that whirl about in the wind, turning anything in their path into burnt ashes.

Write down some powerful words and phrases that capture a fire's power as it rages across a heath or through a forest.

_____

_____

_____

_____

Now turn your words and phrases into an exciting poem about fire. Remember to think about the smells, sights, sounds and feel of the fire.

TEACHER'S NOTES

Introduction

- Load up the Mind's Eye CD-ROM. You may like to tell the children what the title of the session is before you reveal the image, or just open up the picture and watch their initial reactions to it.

- With the whole image in view, elicit the children's first impressions, recording their words on a mind-map on the board. These may be restricted to adjectives, or can be any words and phrases they think of when they look at the picture.

Familiarisation

- Elicit the children's experience of knights. Where have they encountered them before? Talk about books, films, castles, Lego, computer games and so on. Ask them to suggest why it is that we are so interested in knights within history. Why are they such exciting characters?

- Ask the children to consider which might be the hero and which might be the villain in the picture. How can they tell? Which colours do we associate with good and evil? Why?

Exploration

- Ask the class to suggest where they think the knights might be duelling and describe what the rest of the surrounding scenery might be like.

- Draw the children's attention to the sky in the background. In what way does this add to the atmosphere of the picture? Does it make it seem more dramatic? Why? Would the mood of the picture have felt different if the weather had been bright and sunny?

Composite image of knights fighting in storm.
© *John Prior Images/Alamy*

ACTIVITIES

Speaking

- **Thought tracking:** Ask the children to imagine that the knights in the picture are actually actors in a film. This particular scene comes at the end of a very long day's filming and the actors just want to finish and go home! Invite the children to take turns in shouting out what each knight might really be thinking.

Listening

- **Word game:** Sit the class in a large circle and ask them to take turns in calling out a word that describes the sounds of the knights in battle, for example, *clink, bash, groan, wallop, cry, slash.* Encourage them to be as imaginative as possible.

- **Word tennis:** In pairs, invite the children to sit opposite one another. They must take it in turns to 'serve' and then 'return' by calling out a different word that begins with a silent 'k', like 'knight'. When a player hesitates, he or she loses a point. Good examples are: *know, knee, knitting, knife, knot* and *knickers.*

Group Discussion

- **Brainstorming:** Hold a group discussion in which the children are invited to suggest why these two knights might be battling against each other. Share ideas and write some of them down on the board (these could be used for possible story plots). They could be battling over land, power, love, or the Crown.

- **Group talks:** Divide the class into groups of about five or six. Distribute A3 paper and pens to the groups. Ask the children to come up with 10 or more qualities that they believe a knight must have, such as courage, honour and strength.

Drama

- **Group storytelling:** Sit in a large circle and explain to the class that you would like them to take turns in narrating a scene from an imaginary story in which a battle takes place between two knights. Begin with this line and then 'pass it on' around the circle: *It was a dark and stormy night when Sir Lancelot met his enemy on Gibbet Hill...*

Extension

- **Re-enactment:** Ask the children to work together in groups of about five or six. Each group must plan, rehearse and perform a re-enactment of a knights' jousting event. There will be jousts (on foot and pretending!), hog roasts, archery, and dancing. The groups may wish to elect one or more narrators (or jesters) to announce the events and offer commentaries.

Name _____ Date _____

Look again at the image of the brave knights in battle. Imagine there are hundreds more, all fighting for King and Country... and you are one of them!

Write a short poem that describes the sights and sounds of the battlefield. Think carefully about:

- the sound of swords clashing and men shouting

- the feel of the rain-soaked mud beneath your feet

- the sight of more knights charging towards you

- the sound of the wind howling.

Now learn your poem off by heart and perform it to the rest of the class. Remember to use your voice and your body to express yourself in an exciting way that thrills your audience!

TEACHER'S NOTES

Introduction

- Load up the Mind's Eye CD-ROM. You may like to tell the children what the title of the session is before you reveal the image, or just open up the picture and watch their initial reactions to it.

- With the whole image in view, elicit the children's first impressions. Share responses together, noting down key words on the board to be clarified/explored below.

Familiarisation

- Discuss the objects in the image. What sort of map is it? Is it of a place in the world we recognise today? Is anything different? What are these tools and how are they used? (For example, plotting courses, calculating distances, etc.)

- Elicit the children's prior knowledge and experience of maps and map reading. Where and when have they used maps? (On holiday, with road maps, when orienteering or sailing.) Discuss the key features of a map, i.e. compass, key, scale, grid references, labels.

Exploration

- Explore what these items bring to mind. Exploration? A voyage of discovery? Is this a treasure map? How old could the map and tools be? How can we tell?

- To whom might these instruments belong? Encourage the children to suggest names and occupations of people who might read such maps.

Antique nautical map of N. America, Europe and Atlantic Ocean, with compass, magnifying glass and measuring device.
© AGStock USA, Inc./Alamy

ACTIVITIES

Speaking

- **Reporters:** In pairs, the children discuss the distant places they have been to, either on holiday, during a school trip, or having previously lived there. In a final plenary, invite the children to report where their partners have been and collate these places on the board, perhaps on a map if available.

- **Narrate a story:** Seat the class in a large circle. Explain that you are going to narrate a story together by improvising a new line each around the circle. The story will be about a 'voyage of discovery', in which a captain and his crew seek out new lands, making new maps as they go.

Listening

- **Memory game:** Seated in a circle again, invite the children to take turns in reciting the following line: *I went on a voyage of discovery, but all I discovered was a...* . Each person adds a new item, after reciting all the previous ones first!

Group Discussion

- **Class study:** Where would we be without maps? How would we find anywhere? Discuss the world of map making (cartography). How do the children think maps are made? Find out more if you can about how maps are made. Bring in an Ordnance Survey map and discuss its features.

- **Class discussion:** Long ago, when much of our planet still remained undiscovered, it was believed that the Earth was flat and if you travelled far enough into the horizon, you would fall off the edge. Where are the distant frontiers now? Which places do we dream of exploring? Do we really know how the world, the oceans and the universe are mapped out?

Drama

- **Group drama:** In groups of about three or four, the children act out the following scene. They are enjoying playing on the beach when a bottle is washed up, containing a scroll of paper. They discover it is a treasure map. Straight away, the children get searching... What happens next?

Extension

- **Design a map:** In pairs or individually, the children set about designing their own treasure maps, with new oceans and strange lands on them. These will then be presented to the class in a short talk, during which the speaker will highlight different landmarks on the map.

Name _____ Date _____

How well do you know your school? Could you draw a map of it for someone else to follow? Have a go!

Design a map of the school grounds, as if you were looking at them from an aeroplane. Give an idea of the scale by planning the size of the buildings compared to the length of corridors and playgrounds.

When you have finished, exchange your map with a friend and see if you can find your way about!

TEACHER'S NOTES

Introduction

• Load up the Mind's Eye CD-ROM. You may like to tell the children what the title of the session is before you reveal the image, or just open up the picture.

• With the whole image in view, invite the children to share their first impressions and to try to establish what is happening here, based on the evidence before them, i.e. an evening market, in a European city, at Christmas time.

Familiarisation

• Ask the children to look closely at the details in the picture. Where might this be? Look together at the architecture of the buildings. Would they see these buildings in this country or somewhere else in Europe? Has anyone seen buildings like this whilst on holiday somewhere such as Prague, Brussels or Bruges?

• How many colours can the children identify in this picture? How many different buildings?

Exploration

• Can the children imagine the atmosphere of this exciting scene? Invite them to suggest what they might hear if they were standing in the marketplace.

• What do the children think the market stallholders are selling? The tree tells us it may be Christmas time, so is this a Christmas Fair? Could it be an antiques fair?

Grand Place Christmas market at night, Brussels, Belgium.
© PCL/Alamy

ACTIVITIES

Speaking

• **Making sounds:** Explain to the children that you plan to recreate the sound of the Christmas market in the photograph. Firstly brainstorm the sort of sounds one might hear, such as people chatting, sellers calling out offers and deals, Christmas music playing, laughing and joking. Give each child, or group, a particular sound to make, then pretend you are walking through the market.

Listening

• **Reported conversations:** Ask the children to work in pairs. Together they have a discussion about where they might have been for a Christmas holiday or where they would most like to spend Christmas abroad. At the end of the session, ask the children to report what their partners said.

Group Discussion

• **Class discussion:** What do we associate with Christmas? What is a traditional Christmas for us? Invite the children to share customs, traditions and practices that they associate with Christmas. (With luck, these may be from a range of religious, ethnic and social backgrounds.)

• **Group discussion:** In smaller groups this time, ask the children what different sights and sounds a tourist might experience at Christmas time if they visited a city in the UK. How would they know they were somewhere different? (Buildings, food, posters, music, gifts, decorations.)

Drama

• **Advertisement:** In groups of about three or four, ask the children to write, rehearse and perform a short television or radio advertisement promoting this town as a great place to spend Christmas. They will need to focus on the exciting sights, sounds and experiences tourists will enjoy at the annual Christmas market.

• **Group drama:** Divide the class into groups of three or four. Each group is on a family holiday at Christmas time, visiting the evening market. One member of the group becomes lost. How will the others find them? What will happen? The groups role-play the scene. The rest of the class could simulate the sounds of the market each time.

Extension

• **Detective work:** Encourage the children to conduct further research to try to find out where this marketplace may be located. Present them with books, websites, CD-ROMs and atlases that may offer clues by showing them other towns with similar architecture, floodlights and markets.

Name _____   Date _____

Imagine that you are right in the centre of the wonderful market square in the picture. What can you hear? What can you see? How do you feel?

Write down some words and phrases to describe what you can see and hear.

_____

_____

_____

_____

_____

Now put these words and phrases into a poem to be read aloud to your friends. You must make your audience imagine they are there with you, so make your description strong and vivid!

TEACHER'S NOTES

Introduction

- Load up the Mind's Eye CD-ROM. You may like to tell the children what the title of the session is before you reveal the image, or just open up the picture and watch their initial reactions to it.

- With the whole image in view, introduce and discuss the word 'maze'. What does it mean? Agree on a definition, e.g. 'a puzzling network of paths or hedges through which one must find a way'.

Familiarisation

- Elicit the children's own experience and knowledge of mazes. Has anyone visited a maze? Has anyone actually lost their way in a maze? How did they feel?

- Do the children think the two people in the image are lost? How can we tell? What does their body language tell us (woman looking into distance/man standing, hands on hips)?

Exploration

- Using a mind-map or 'spidergram' on the board, brainstorm possible captions for this image. Think of single words or short phrases that sum up what is happening in the picture (e.g. Lost! Help! 'I told you it was the other way, but you wouldn't listen!').

- Ask the children to imagine they were hovering in a helicopter above this maze. What would it look like? Ask the children to draw a quick sketch to show what this section of the maze, and perhaps the whole maze itself, might look like.

Two people lost in Glendurgan Maze, Nr Falmouth, Cornwall.
© Robert Harding Picture Library/Alamy

ACTIVITIES

Speaking

- **Talking partners:** Ask the children to work in pairs and pretend to be the characters in the photograph. They are lost and each of them blames the other for their predicament. Invite the pairs to practise and perform a short sketch in which the characters argue initially and then come up with a plan to find a way out.

Listening

- **Hot seating:** Invite volunteers to sit in the 'hot seat' and answer questions from the floor, in the role of either the man or the woman. Again, the characters could blame the other for taking a wrong turn in the maze, but if this is the case, they must be prepared to justify why their own plan would have been better!

- **Word game:** Working in pairs, ask the children to take turns in sharing how they might feel if they were lost in a maze. Each speaker must suggest one word that sums up their feelings each time. Examples to get them started are: *confused, worried, puzzled* and *amazed*.

Group Discussion

- **Which way?:** Ask the children to form small groups of three or four. Each group imagines they are lost in a maze together. They must try to agree on a way out (but initially each person wants to take a different path out of there!). How will they resolve it? Should they split up and try different routes or should they keep together and try each option systematically?

Drama

- **Thought tracking:** Ask for two volunteers (perhaps rotate turns around the class) to stand at the front and strike similar poses to the characters in the photograph. Invite the rest of the class to suggest suitable lines for each person, while the actors hold their positions.

- **Whole class:** Using a large area (perhaps the hall or playground), ask the children to try making their own real maze, using themselves as hedges! The children link arms to form continuous lines and curves. Ask for a brave volunteer to test the maze.

Extension

- **Investigate and design:** Why were mazes invented? When were the first mazes established in the grounds of stately homes? Write a set of instructions for maze builders to build your perfect maze. Work singly or in pairs.

DID YOU HEAR THAT?

You are lost in a maze with your friend when you suddenly hear the strangest noise – a growl – and it's getting louder. Something, or someone, is in the maze with you.

Write, and then perform, the conversation you might have with your friend as you decide what you should do next.

_____

_____

_____

_____

_____

_____

_____

_____

_____

_____

_____

_____

TEACHER'S NOTES

Introduction

- Load up the Mind's Eye CD-ROM. You may like to tell the children what the title of the session is before you reveal the image, or just open up the picture and watch their initial reactions to it.

- With the whole image in view, elicit the children's first impressions of the practice of painting faces in this way. Have the children ever seen this before? Does anyone know where in the world this custom is practised, and why? (A Japanese symbol of tradition and native culture, signalling beauty and wealth.)

Familiarisation

- Elicit the children's knowledge and experience of painted faces, such as clowns, masks, make-up, face-painting activities, tribal war paint and so on.

- Look together at the girls' hair and clothes. Could this be part of a ceremony of some sort? Do they look like normal everyday clothes? Would the children in the class like to dress in such a fashion?

Exploration

- Divide the class into groups of about four or five and invite them to consider different customs and traditions around the world that others might find strange, but are part of a nation's heritage. Is there any similar sort of custom the children practise as part of their own religious or national heritage?

- The girls look wise and thoughtful. What might they be thinking? Invite the children to suggest the thoughts that might be running through the girls' heads.

Young girls in costume at the Jidai Matsun Festival of Ages, an annual festival held on 22nd October in Kyoto, Japan, to celebrate the city's long history. © Nigel Hicks/Alamy

ACTIVITIES

Speaking

- **Expressions:** How much do we reveal through our faces? Seat the class in a large circle. Ask for volunteers to take turns to choose a particular emotion and then try to express that feeling through their facial expressions. For the person to have succeeded, the class must guess how they are feeling just from looking at their face; for example: *nervous, frightened, proud, surprised, upset* and *angry*.

Listening

- **Circle game:** Explain to the class that they are going to play a game in which they will practise expressing their emotions through their faces only. Call out a number along a scale between 1 and 5, where 1 is very sad and 5 is very happy. Each time you call out a number, the children must reflect that emotion through their faces and then hold that expression for you to see!

Group Discussion

- **Class discussion:** What do clothes, haircuts, make-up and jewellery say about us? Should we judge people on what they wear or on what's inside? Discuss with the children why, as we get older, many of us become interested in fashion.

- **Class debate:** How would the world be if everyone dressed the same? Would it be dull or would it make life fairer? Invite the children to cxonsider why a uniform is so often worn in schools. Who likes wearing it? What happens when uniform is not worn? Do children have to think more carefully about what to wear?

Drama

- **Paired role-play:** In pairs, ask the children to prepare a short piece of drama in which one person makes different facial expressions into a pretend mirror as the other person mirrors their expressions, sitting opposite them.

- **Duologues:** Ask the children to imagine they are walking down a street when they suddenly see someone who looks exactly like them (a 'doppelganger'). In pairs, they act out a scene when the two identical people meet.

Extension

- **Mask-making:** Invite the children to make simple masks to wear over their faces so that only their eyes are revealed. Then ask everyone to put their masks on and walk about the room, so that the children no longer know where their friends are! Ask each child to turn to the person nearest to them and guess who is hiding behind the mask using only their eyes as clues!

Name _____ Date _____

I'M SURE I KNOW YOU!

Imagine if you had a 'doppelganger', a person who looks just like you! How would you feel if you bumped into that person in the street?

Write a short conversation between you and your doppelganger, and then find a friend to perform it with to the class.

_____

_____

_____

_____

_____

_____

_____

_____

_____

_____

_____

TEACHER'S NOTES

Introduction

- Load up the Mind's Eye CD-ROM. You may like to tell the children what the title of the session is before you reveal the image, or just open up the picture.

- With the whole image in view, elicit the children's first impressions of the scene and establish that it is a picture of five pilots walking to, or from, their aeroplanes on an airfield. Ask the question: *When was this photograph taken?*

Familiarisation

- Discuss black and white photographs. Explain how colour was only introduced in more recent years, so this might be a scene from some time ago. Look closely at the image. Is the aeroplane old or new? How can we tell? Look also at the pilots' clothes and equipment. Does it look old or new?

- Elicit the children's knowledge and experience of aeroplanes. Which types of aircraft have they flown in? Do they think the aeroplane in the shot is a domestic passenger airliner or a war plane? Could these be military pilots, in the RAF or American Air Force?

Exploration

- Where do the children think the pilots might have come from? Are they returning from an historic air battle? Can we glean anything from their facial expressions or their body language?

- What might the pilots be looking at? Do you think they have a welcome committee, all cheering them home? Or perhaps they are about to climb into their planes, with just a few other soldiers to wave them off. Where might they be heading?

WWII British airforce bomber crew. From left–right, Observer, Wireless Operator, Rear Gunner, Second Pilot, Pilot Captain.
© Davis/Hulton Archive/Getty Images

ACTIVITIES

👄 Speaking

- **Emotions:** Seat the children in a large circle. Ask them to imagine they are the pilots in the picture, about to board their war planes to go into battle. Ask each child to offer a word to sum up how they might be feeling. (You may wish to talk first about courage, doing your duty, serving your country and so on.)

- **Memory game:** In the same circle, initiate a new game in which the children must take turns to complete the following line: *If I could fly, way up high, in the sky, I'd travel to...* (fill in a country or place of their choosing). The next person must repeat the line and all the previous destinations, adding one more.

👂 Listening

- **Reporting:** Ask the children to divide into pairs. Partner A shares their thoughts and feelings about becoming a fighter pilot. Would they like to? How would they feel? Partner B listens carefully. Then, in a final plenary, partner B reports A's feelings and thoughts to the class as accurately as possible, then swap the pair round.

👁 Group Discussion

- **Group conversations:** Divide the class into groups of five if possible (four will do). Ask them to imagine they are the pilots in the picture. They have just returned from a dangerous mission. They share their feelings with each other and recall the events that happened along the way. These conversations could be performed at the end.

🎭 Drama

- **Hot seating:** Invite volunteers to take the 'hot seat' at the front of the class and answer questions in the character of one of the pilots in the picture. Each person can explain where they have been or where they are going to and how they feel about the mission.

- **Group drama:** Ask the children to get into groups of about three or four. Each group must pretend they are on a plane together – either involved in a battle, or on a domestic flight – when something goes badly wrong. They struggle to control the plane but are forced to put on their parachutes and escape.

❗ Extension

- **Presentation:** Invite the children to work together in pairs or small groups, researching the subject of aeroplanes. They should explore their history, different types, designs and uses. They may use a range of resources including Internet sites, CD-ROMs, books and magazines.

Name _____ Date _____

THANK HEAVENS FOR FLIGHT!

Your task is to give a short speech to the class on why we should be thankful that aeroplanes have been invented.

You will need to think about how flight has changed so many aspects of our lives, including:

- holidays
- emergency rescues
- business trips
- space exploration
- communications
- faster deliveries.

Write some notes to help you remember what to say.

_____

_____

_____

_____

_____

_____

_____

_____

_____

_____

_____

TEACHER'S NOTES

Introduction

- Load up the Mind's Eye CD-ROM. You may like to tell the children what the title of the session is before you reveal the image, or just open up the picture and watch their initial reactions to it.

- With the whole image in view, elicit the children's first impressions of the scene. What might lie beyond the balustrade? Is he a stunt cyclist? How exactly did he get to this position?

Familiarisation

- Discuss the image further, assessing the location (mountains in the background, pine trees etc.). Invite the children to guess where in the world this might be.

- Elicit the children's prior knowledge and experience of stunt bikes. What do they know about this sport? What sort of cycling do the children do?

Exploration

- The cyclist looks to be pulling stunts and tricks in a precarious location! Can the children think of other dangerous places that would prove interesting venues for bike stunts (not to be tried at home!).

- Can the children think of different occupations that involve cycling? Record these on the board together. Good examples include postwoman, courier and police officer.

Mountain bike stunts viewed through a fish-eye lens.
© Westend61/Alamy

ACTIVITIES

🗣 Speaking

- **Captions:** Invite the children to work in groups of three or four. The task is to discuss and write down different captions that could be written beneath this image. Ask a group spokesperson to present these suggestions back to the class in a final plenary.

- **Talking pairs:** Where would be the best place to enjoy a biking holiday? Where would be the worst? Ask the children to respond to these questions, working in pairs, and writing down some suggestions to give back to the class at the end.

👂 Listening

- **Listening game:** In an open area, ask the children to spread out and find some space. The idea of this game is that you call out different ways of travelling and each time the pupils must do the actions that are associated with that form of transport, e.g. cycling (pedalling), driving (steering), skiing (holding skis), etc. The last person to do the actions must sit out each time.

👁 Group Discussion

- **Class discussion:** What do the children know about the history of the bicycle? Elicit the children's prior knowledge of the bicycle and invite them to guess how long it has been around. Establish together where such information could be found, i.e. Internet sites, books, encyclopaedias, CD-ROMs.

- **Class debate:** Should more people be getting on a bike and cycling to work or to the shops? Are we relying on cars too much? Have we become too lazy? What about the environment? Initiate a discussion on the benefits of cycling instead of driving to places. (This will be good preparatory work for the task below.)

🎭 Drama

- **Television advertisement:** Ask the children to work in pairs or small groups, designing, writing and performing a short advertisement for television in which they seek to persuade viewers to get on a bike more, and leave the car at home. Encourage them to list the benefits of cycling over driving: healthier, cheaper, better for the environment, more fun, quicker in traffic etc.

🚶 Extension

- **Research/presentation:** Following on from the group discussion, ask the children to work in pairs to find out more about the history of the bicycle and present their findings to the class.

Name _____ Date _____

WHAT DO YOU THINK YOU'RE DOING?

Imagine you are the cyclist in the picture when a police officer asks you why you are riding your bike in such a dangerous way in a public place. What will you say?

Write a short conversation in which you try to explain to the police officer what you were doing and offer an apology. Remember to be polite and charming at all times!

Officer: _____

_____

You: _____

_____

_____

Officer: _____

_____

You: _____

_____

_____

Officer: _____

_____

Find a partner to be the police officer and perform your script to the rest of the class.

TEACHER'S NOTES

Introduction

• Load up the Mind's Eye CD-ROM. You may like to tell the children what the title of the session is before you reveal the image, or just open up the picture and watch their initial reactions to it.

• With the whole image in view, elicit the children's first impressions of the scene. Is it a painting or a photograph? How can we tell?

Familiarisation

• Discuss the features in the picture. Is the tower an early lighthouse, a lookout post, or a gun tower? What is the smaller object next to the building? Could it be two people, pointing at the ship? Is this area a haven for smugglers?

• Discuss whether the ship in the picture may have struck rocks, or whether it is just sitting at low tide.

Exploration

• Explore together what the lights in the distance might be from. Could this be what the two characters (mentioned before) are pointing to? Could the lights be from a distant lighthouse?

• Explore the mood and tone of the image together. Share and collate words and phrases that might describe the atmosphere of the scene on the board. Good examples are *eerie, mysterious, thunderclouds, jagged rocks*.

Moonlit landscape painted in oils by Russian artist, Ivan Aivazovsky, in 1863.
© Sotherby's/akg-images

ACTIVITIES

Speaking

• **Narrate a story:** Seat the class in a large circle and explain that you would like to begin a story about a gang of smugglers. One stormy night their ship strikes rocks and they are forced to jump overboard. Begin the story and then invite everyone to add a line as it moves around the circle.

Listening

• **Memory game:** Seated in a large circle again, the children take turns to say the following line: *If I went to sea, I'd take with me... .* The children must add an item that they would wish to take on a sea voyage with them. The next person must recite the line and all the previous items, before adding another one of their own.

• **Circle game:** Sit the class in a large circle again and explain the rules of this game. Each person takes a turn to say the following line out loud: *Aye, aye, Captain!* The aim is to disguise one's voice while the others in the team, seated with their eyes closed, must decide who spoke. Choose the children by tapping them on the head/shoulder.

👁 Group Discussion

• **Class discussion:** Discuss the idea of smuggling. Look at its definition and context. Elicit the children's prior knowledge of smugglers from films and books that they may be familiar with. What sort of items did sailors smuggle? How did they approach the mainland? Where might they have kept their stash?

• **Group discussion:** Divide the class into groups of three or four. Present each group with the following task: they must compile a list of reasons why coastal resorts are so popular for holidaymakers. Why do we like spending so much time at the seaside? What is it about the sea that fascinates us as a class? After a few minutes, return together and share feedback.

🎭 Drama

• **Group play:** In groups of about four or five, the children role-play a scene in which they are pirates, looking for somewhere on the coast to stash their stolen treasure. A storm throws their ship off course as they approach the rocks on the coast. How will they save themselves and their treasure?

❗ Extension

• **Poetry:** Working individually, ask the children to draft, edit and then perform their own poems inspired by the picture (see activity sheet). Encourage them to learn their poems off by heart so that they can perform them to the class, using lots of facial expression and voice intonation!

Name _____ Date _____

THE HIGH SEAS

Look again at the picture. Think about the sights, sounds and feel of the waves, the dark clouds overhead and the wind that is blowing from across the ocean.

Write down some words and phrases that describe these thoughts. Use as many adjectives as you can.

_____

_____

_____

_____

_____

Now turn these words and phrases into a poem about the sea. Learn the words off by heart and perform your poem for the class.

TEACHER'S NOTES

Introduction

- Load up the Mind's Eye CD-ROM. You may like to tell the children what the title of the session is before you reveal the image, or just open up the picture and watch their initial reactions to it.

- With the whole image in view, elicit the children's first impressions, recording their words on a mind-map on the board. These may be the first words and phrases that come to mind when they look at the picture.

Familiarisation

- Ask the children to consider the features of this image: how many soldiers there are; what the occasion might be; where it is taking place; what regiment they may be from.

- Invite the children to share past experiences they have had of similar occasions. Has anyone seen soldiers like these before? Where and when? What was it like?

Exploration

- Now talk about what the soldiers remind them of: toy soldiers; a row of dominoes; clockwork figures; the grand old Duke of York. Encourage the children to use their imaginations when looking at the photograph, to move beyond saying what they see to saying what they think about when they look at the soldiers in a row.

- Although photos don't talk, this one conjures up different sounds in one's mind. Ask the children to describe the sounds they can hear when they look at the image. You can start them off with: bugles sounding; feet stomping, sergeant screaming (see activity sheet).

Trooping the Colour ceremony. The parade in front of the Queen takes place in London each June.
© David Levenson/Alamy

ACTIVITIES

Speaking

- **Talking partners:** Working in pairs, ask the children to pretend to be two soldiers on the day of the parade. It is early in the morning and they are sharing their thoughts about what lies ahead. For one soldier, this is his last parade as he is about to retire. For the other, this is his first parade and he is feeling nervous!

Listening

- **Hot seating:** Invite volunteers to sit in the 'hot seat' and answer questions from the floor, in the role of a soldier from the photo. Ask the class to make notes each time. After a few volunteers have spoken, quiz them to see if they were listening to the different answers.

- **Chinese whispers:** Lining up in two parallel lines (two rows of soldiers), take turns in sending a message down one line and back up the other. Did the message change as it moved along? Were people listening carefully enough?

 Group Discussion

- **Debate:** In groups of five or six, or as a class, invite the children to share their ideas about what the purpose of these parades might be. What exactly are they for? Are they for tourists? Or are they for the sake of tradition? Are they worth the expense? Are they to make us feel proud?

- **Planning committee:** Ask the children, in small groups, to imagine they are the planning committee for this parade. It is a week before the big day and they have just heard that the weather forecast is for torrential rain. What plans will they put in place? How will they cope? Can they put a plan together so that they are ready for the rain?

Drama

- **Thought tracking:** Ask for six volunteers to line up side by side like soldiers on parade. Ask them to stand as still as statues, but to display very different facial expressions. You may wish to instruct them to smile/grimace/look sleepy/look nauseous, etc. Then invite the rest of the group to voice the thoughts that may be going through each soldier's head.

Extension

- **Group drama:** Practise trying to march in step with each other – it's not as easy as you think! Create some space (or use the hall/playground) and practise marching together in time to a steady beat. Invite the children to share their responses to the task. Was it easy or hard? Could they do it for hours at a time?

THE SOLDIER RAP

Working in small groups, compose and then perform your very own rap song, or rhythmical poem, about soldiers marching on parade. You can lay down the beat by chanting 'left, right, left, right, left… !'

CHORUS	VERSE 1	VERSE 2
_____	_____	_____
_____	_____	_____
_____	_____	_____
_____	_____	_____
_____	_____	_____
_____	_____	_____

STORMY WEATHER

The day of the parade is here, but a giant thundercloud appears overhead. The rain pelts down and the wind knocks people off their feet.

Write and perform a sketch in which a television reporter describes the scene and talks to people caught in the storm.

Reporter: _____

Tourist 1: _____

Reporter: _____

Soldier: _____

Reporter: _____

Tourist 2: _____

TEACHER'S NOTES

Introduction

• Load up the Mind's Eye CD-ROM. You may like to tell the children what the title of the session is before you reveal the image, or just open up the picture and watch their initial reactions to it.

• With the whole image in view, elicit the children's first impressions of the scene. Allow them to share their general observations and feelings with the class.

Familiarisation

• Focus on the atmosphere and mood of the setting. Identify what makes it a 'spooky' scene. Obvious clues include: a turret in the shape of a witch's hat, storm clouds, a gnarled tree, overgrown steps, swirling mist, dark windows.

• Brainstorm, using a mind-map or spidergram on the board, any descriptive words and phrases that spring to mind when the children look at the image. For example: *eerie, creepy, spooky, mysterious.*

Exploration

• Invite the children to imagine whose house this might be. Encourage them to take turns in making up ghostly folktales and legends associated with the house and gardens.

• In pairs, ask the children to think of possible names for this old house, listing the names on a sheet of paper ready to share with the class at the end.

Ecclescrieg House, Kincardineshire, Scotland.
© The Marsden Archive/Alamy

ACTIVITIES

👄 Speaking

• **Duologue:** Divide the class into pairs. One person pretends to be knocking on the door of the great house and the other replies with some frightening sounds. The children swap roles and continue to take turns for five minutes. Then ask the pairs to share some of their sounds from 'behind the door'.

• **Reciting poems:** Ask the children to write and perform their own spooky poems, based on the images in the picture. You may wish to help them get started by reading poems of this kind. Good ones include: 'The Listeners' by Walter de la Mare and 'The Witch' by Jack Prelutsky.

👂 Listening

• **Spooky sounds:** Divide the class into groups of three or four. Each group must prepare a one-minute sequence of sound effects that might be heard inside the great hall. Then invite each group to perform their sounds, as the rest of the children close their eyes and pretend they are entering the house for the first time. Examples are: creaky floorboards, footsteps, laughter, screams, whispers, thuds.

👁 Group Discussion

• **Group narration:** For the following task the children can work as a whole class, or in groups of five or six. Ask the children to sit in a circle and take turns narrating an improvised story about the witch's house in the picture. Begin with an opening line for the story and then move around the circle, each person moving the story on by adding another line of narration.

🎭 Drama

• **Duologue:** Ask the children to get into pairs to perform a role-play in which two friends are chatting. One friend is really keen to visit an old, deserted house located in the woods near their home. The other thinks it could be too spooky and needs persuading! Ask the children to prepare and then perform the conversation they might have. Will they go?

• **Group drama:** In small groups, the children pretend they are exploring the old house. They enter through the main door, but then suddenly it slams shut behind them and they are locked inside. What happens next? Will they panic? Or will someone remain calm and find a different way out? Invite the groups to prepare and perform a short sketch for the class.

Extension

• **Group drama:** Consider the house from the owner's point of view. Ask the children to imagine they live alone in this great hall. They don't like being disturbed and they definitely don't like being thought of as a witch! One day some children come prowling around, making nuisances of themselves. The owner decides to take action to get rid of them. Ask the children to act out this story in group plays.

YOU'LL NEVER GUESS WHAT I'VE SEEN!

Imagine you and a friend have been to explore the strange house in the picture. You find some very frightening surprises inside and once you are home you tell your Mum all about what happened.

Write and then perform the conversation you might have with your Mum. At first, she probably won't believe you!

You: _____

_____

_____

Mum: _____

_____

_____

You: _____

_____

_____

Mum: _____

_____

_____

You: _____

_____

Remember: If you want to explore real haunted houses, never go alone!

TEACHER'S NOTES

Introduction

- Load up the Mind's Eye CD-ROM. You may like to tell the children what the title of the session is before you reveal the image, or just open up the picture and watch their initial reactions to it.

- With the whole image in view, elicit the children's first impressions of the scene. Establish that it is a stone circle. Has anyone seen this before? What is its name?

Familiarisation

- Look closely at the image. How can we appreciate the size of the stones (i.e. see people on left for scale)? Establish that this is called Stonehenge and that it is a man-made stone circle dating back thousands of years. It is one of the most important historical sites in the world.

- Does anyone know where Stonehenge is located? Invite the children to guess its location. Establish that it is situated on Salisbury Plain in Wiltshire, Southern England.

Exploration

- Ask questions: e.g. *Why was it built? How did they manage to use such large stones?* (Stones such as these would be a colossal weight – and there were no cranes in those days!) Introduce and discuss the idea of druids, solstice, temple etc.

- Invite the children to look closely at the sky. Is this real? How could it be a pink colour? Encourage the pupils to suggest the time of day this photograph was taken.

Stonehenge, Salisbury Plain, Wiltshire.
© nagelstock.com/Alamy

ACTIVITIES

👄 Speaking

- **Brainstorm:** Ask the children to imagine they are standing alone in the centre of the stone circle as evening is drawing in. How would they feel? Ask for words/phrases to describe their feelings and the sights and sounds they might experience. Record these words and phrases on a mind-map on the board.

- **Paired work:** Explain that the image is a striking one, partly because of the dramatic skies. Ask the children to work in pairs, making short notes on how different skies might affect the mood of the place. Write down other weather scenarios and next to each record some adjectives to describe how the mood has changed, e.g. *summer sun: relaxed, soothing, spiritual; snow: frozen, lonely, magical; storm: barren, cold, hard, inhospitable.*

👂 Listening

- **Reported conversations:** In pairs, invite the children to share their experiences of stone circles and other ancient sites that they may have visited on holiday or during a school trip. Good examples include Roman settlements, churches and temples, pyramids, other henges, etc. Each partner must then report the other person's experiences back to the class in a final plenary.

👁 Group Discussion

- **Class discussion:** When humans work together the results can often be astonishing, like Stonehenge! Invite the children to think of other great achievements that have only been made possible through teamwork (space exploration, building the pyramids). Discuss the qualities we need for a team to be effective: *co-operation, patience, friendliness, understanding.*

🎭 Drama

- **Group work:** Explain to the class that you would like them to design and create their own stone circle using themselves! Find a large space (grass, or hall with floor mats) and ask the children to share ideas for the shape of the circle and then simulate it together. (Note: placing stones horizontally may be dangerous!)

- **Group drama:** Divide the class into small groups. Explain the plot for the group plays: the children are on a walk that leads past Stonehenge. As they approach the stones a terrible storm brews and as the lightning strikes around them, a ghostly druid appears among the stones. What happens next?

❗ Extension

- **Presentation:** Working in pairs, ask the class to find out more about Stonehenge, and/or other similar stone circles. They may use websites, CD-ROMs, books and magazines. Once they have collected enough information, encourage the children to make some notes for a short presentation to the class (see activity sheet).

Name _____ Date _____

THE HISTORY OF THE STONES

Can you imagine how difficult it must have been to construct Stonehenge without using cranes and lorries? Find out more about how these stones came to be here using websites, CD-ROMs, encyclopaedias, books and magazines.

Think about:

- how old the site is
- who constructed it, and how
- what it was used for
- other similar sites around the world.

Use the space below to make some notes. When you are ready, share what you have researched in a short presentation to the class.

_____

_____

_____

_____

_____

_____

_____

_____

_____

TEACHER'S NOTES

Introduction

- Load up the Mind's Eye CD-ROM. You may like to tell the children what the title of the session is before you reveal the image, or just open up the picture and watch their initial reactions to it.

- With the whole image in view, elicit the children's first impressions of the scene. What might we call the plate-shaped object? Does anyone know what 'UFO' actually stands for?

Familiarisation

- Elicit the children's knowledge and experience of UFOs. Why do we often think of them as plate shapes? Would they actually be this shape? Why?

- What else is in the picture? Is the ship in space? Is that the Earth that we can see in the bottom left-hand corner? What do the children think might be causing the swirling mists and strange lights?

Exploration

- Invite the children to imagine that they had seen this UFO in the sky. How would they feel? Record some key words on the board in a mind-map, to illustrate how UFOs make us feel, for example: *excited, frightened, curious, brave, imaginative, cautious, gullible.*

- Many people have managed to create realistic images of fake UFOs, some by throwing a plate into the air and photographing it! Ask the children to consider how this image could have been made.

UFO approaching planet (digital image).
© Adrian Neal/Stone/Getty Images

ACTIVITIES

Speaking

- **News reports:** In pairs, ask the children to write, rehearse and perform a news item reporting the sighting of this UFO in our skies. One person can be the 'anchor man' in the newsroom, and the other can be the roving reporter, sent out to investigate where and when the UFO was seen.

- **Circle game:** Seat the class in a large circle. The children take turns to complete the line: *If I went up in a UFO I would take with me... .* Each person adds a possession of their choosing, but must recite all those that have gone before it first!

Listening

- **Secret sounds:** Seat the class in a circle again. This time ask everyone to close their eyes. Move around the circle and touch children on the back to let them know it is their turn. Their task is to emit an 'alien-type' noise and then everyone else must guess who made the sound.

Group Discussion

- **Group debate:** Do aliens exist? Are there really such things as UFOs? Either in groups or as a whole class, initiate a discussion in which the children are free to share their views on UFOs. You might like to introduce and reinforce key vocabulary, including: *galaxy, universe, life form* and the names of the planets.

Drama

- **Telephone conversations:** In pairs, one child imagines they have seen the UFO in the picture and immediately telephones a friend with the news. The person on the end of the line does not believe them. When the children have prepared their scenes, ask them to perform them, seated back to back, holding imaginary telephones.

- **Group drama:** It is an ordinary school day, in the middle of a Maths lesson. Suddenly, someone notices a very strange sight outside: it is a vast alien spaceship and it seems to be heading straight for the school! In groups, or as a whole class, complete the story and enact this scenario.

Extension

- **Presentation:** Ask the children to work in pairs. Their task is to design their very own alien spaceship on a large sheet of paper. Once they have carefully drawn and labelled it, they must present their design to the class, explaining the features of their craft.

Name _____ Date _____

With a partner, take the roles of an alien from a distant galaxy and a human being from Earth. The human must explain to the alien how to play their favourite sport or game.

Think of the questions an alien might ask and make some notes to help the human answer them.

Remember: the alien has never been to Earth before, so the human will have to explain EVERYTHING from the beginning!

_____

_____

_____

_____

_____

_____

_____

_____

_____

_____

_____

TEACHER'S NOTES

Introduction

• Load up the Mind's Eye CD-ROM. You may like to tell the children what the title of the session is before you reveal the image, or just open up the picture and watch their initial reactions to it.

• With the whole image in view, invite the children to share their responses to the scene. Discuss what is happening and why the person might be in the cave. Is she pot-holing, attempting a cave rescue, a scientist or a geologist, maybe?

Familiarisation

• Encourage the children to look closely at the image. Analyse together where the light is coming from, how deep the water appears to be, what the person is wearing, why water seems to be dropping from above.

• Elicit the children's prior knowledge and experience of caves. Where have they seen them? What is pot-holing? Why do people enjoy exploring small spaces underground?

Exploration

• Discuss together where this cave entrance may lead. Where do they think the person might be heading? Where could this cave be located? Could it be by the sea? How can we tell?

• Ask the children to share words and phrases that could be used to describe the atmosphere inside the cave. Brainstorm these ideas by recording words on a mind-map. Start with: *echoes, damp walls, sound of drips, sloshing water, slimy, slippery surfaces.*

Female caver in a cave streamway, Ogof Ffynnon Ddu1, South Wales. © *Chris Howes/Wild Places Photography/Alamy*

ACTIVITIES

Speaking

• **Story narration:** Seat the class in a large circle. Begin narrating an improvised story in which someone becomes lost or trapped inside a cave on the coast. The tide is rising and the light from outside is fading. Invite each child to contribute a line to the story as you move around the circle.

• **Hot seating:** Invite volunteers to take turns sitting in the 'hot seat' at the front of the class and answer questions in the role of the person in the cave. Some questions to begin with could be: *Why are you in the cave? What does it feel like to be in such a confined space? How do you feel when you finally see the sunlight again? Have you ever become trapped in a cave?*

Listening

• **Cave sounds:** In pairs or small groups, ask the children to try to simulate the sounds that might accompany this picture. Once they are ready, the children can perform their sound effects to the rest of the class. Sounds could include: water sloshing around, dripping noise, someone calling with an echo repeating, sound of footsteps, banging on a rock wall.

Group Discussion

• **Class discussion:** Begin a discussion about the pleasures, and dangers, of playing by the sea: the importance of having fun, but being sensible at the same time! Exploring coastal caves is great fun, but you must keep a careful eye on the tide. Has anyone in the class had a nasty experience of nearly being cut off by a rising tide? Reinforce the need to take care by the sea.

• **Group discussion:** Divide the class into small groups of about three or four. Provide each group with a sheet of paper and a pen. The task is to make a list of the sorts of things one might need on a caving expedition. They may begin with the items they can see in the image, and then think of more, such as hard hat with torch attached, rucksack, waterproof overalls.

Drama

• **Paired conversations:** Ask the children to get into pairs for this role-play. The task is to perform a short sketch in which one person plays the part of the person in the scene and the other assumes the role of a person trapped deeper inside the cave. The partners perform a conversation by shouting across the room.

Extension

• **Group drama:** Divide the class into groups of three or four. Each group must prepare and perform a short sketch in which a group of friends are exploring the caves and rock pools on a stretch of coastline. They lose track of time and realise that the tide is rising. Unless they hurry, the entrance to their cave may be cut off completely. How will they complete the scene?

I DON'T WANT TO GO!

Imagine you and a claustrophobic (scared of small spaces) friend are on a caving trip.

Write and then perform a short conversation in which you try to persuade your nervous partner to be brave and come into the cave.

You: _____

_____

_____

Friend: _____

_____

_____

You: _____

_____

_____

Friend: _____

_____

_____

You: _____

_____

TEACHER'S NOTES

Introduction

- Load up the Mind's Eye CD-ROM. You may like to tell the children what the title of the session is before you reveal the image, or just open up the picture and watch their initial reactions to it.

- With the whole image in view, invite the children to explain why there are so many balloons. Is it a race or exhibition of some sort? Have they just taken off or are they landing?

Familiarisation

- How many balloons are in the picture? How many different colours? Which balloon has the greatest number of different colours on it? Which are the children's favourite balloons?

- Elicit the children's prior knowledge and experience of hot air balloons. Has anyone been in one? Where and when do you usually see them? How do they manage to stay in the air?

Exploration

- Explore with the children what it might feel like to be up in a hot air balloon. Brainstorm some key adjectives on the board: *peaceful, windy, bright, quiet, magical.*

- Invite the children to use their imaginations to see the balloons as different objects. What could they be (beachballs, marbles, bubbles in the air, Christmas baubles)?

Hot air balloons in flight.
© Comstock Images/Alamy

ACTIVITIES

Speaking

- **Hot seating:** Invite volunteers to sit at the front of the class, in the 'hot seat', and answer questions from everyone about what it felt like to be in the balloon race in the picture. They must try to describe the experience as vividly as they can, using all their senses and a lot of imagination.

- **Telephone conversations:** Invite the children, in twos, to sit back to back. They are two friends in the middle of a telephone conversation in which one is trying to persuade the other to come ballooning with him or her. The other is timid and has a fear of heights. What will each one say to the other?

Listening

- **Talking to an alien:** In pairs, the children take turns to explain the practice of hot air ballooning to an alien who has just landed on Earth. Fortunately the alien can communicate with us freely, but has no concept whatsoever of ballooning. The alien must listen carefully and ask for further definitions and explanations wherever necessary.

Group Discussion

- **Research:** Divide the children into groups of about three or four. Each group has 10 minutes to pool the knowledge they currently have on hot air balloons. Their task is to try to explain to the rest of the class how they work. After 10 minutes, share ideas and theories (in preparation for the Extension task below).

Drama

- **Contrasts:** In pairs, the children prepare a short sketch in which two friends go ballooning. One friend suffers from terrible vertigo (fear of heights) and huddles in a corner of the basket; the other loves heights and looks happily over the edge! The pupils role-play a conversation between the two characters.

- **Group drama:** In small groups, the children pretend they are all in the basket of a hot air balloon. Unfortunately they are losing altitude and something must be done. Encourage some of the group members to be calm, others nervous and panicking. What will they do to stay in the air? Will they have to crash land? Each group prepares, rehearses and performs their piece.

Extension

- **Group presentation:** Encourage the children to prepare a short group presentation on how a hot air balloon manages to stay in the air. The resources available to them may include the Internet, CD-ROMs and encyclopaedias.

Name _____ Date _____

IF I COULD FLY...

Prepare a short speech to give to the class in which you explain what you would do, and where you would go, if you could fly like a bird.

Make notes to help you remember what to say when you make your speech.

_____

_____

_____

_____

_____

_____

_____

_____

_____

_____

_____

_____

TEACHER'S NOTES

Introduction

• Load up the Mind's Eye CD-ROM. You may like to tell the children what the title of the session is before you reveal the image, or just open up the picture and watch their initial reactions to it.

• With the whole image in view, elicit the children's first impressions of the scene. What has happened? Is the girl actually locked out? If so, why? Or is the girl just spying through the letter box for fun? Does she live here, or is she calling for a friend?

Familiarisation

• Establish that the girl is looking through a letter box. Ask the children if they have ever done this. Would they recognise their own homes from this viewpoint? Ask them to think about what they would be able to see in their own houses from the letter box.

• What type of house is this? What sort of street could it be situated on? Are there any clues in the picture? (Steps, porch, number 607 suggests a very long road.)

Exploration

• Invite the children to think of some good captions to write underneath this image. Some suggestions are: *Let me in! I can see you! Can Lucy come out to play? I need the toilet, help!*

• In pairs, ask the children to consider what the dog might be thinking. Is this his favourite spot? Is he wanting to get inside also? Is he in trouble too, or is he guarding the child?

Girl with Pomeranian dog looking through letter box, Los Angeles, California, USA.
© Wendy Ashton/Taxi/Getty Images

ACTIVITIES

Speaking

• **Reported conversations:** Ask the children to get into pairs. Each pair must swap or make up stories about times when they or their parents forgot their keys and could not get into their house or car. Or perhaps they have called for a friend, but couldn't attract their attention inside the house. Invite the children to report back to the class, explaining what happened to their partner.

• **Improvised lines:** Draw a large letter box on the board, at the right height for the children to reach. Ask for volunteers to come up to the board, peer 'through' the letter box and shout out something to the imaginary people inside!

Listening

• **Who's that?:** Cut a small letter-box-shaped hole in a large piece of paper. Invite the children to take turns to hide behind the hole, with just their eyes showing. Ask for volunteers to guess who is hiding 'behind the door', based on the pair of eyes, and a spoken word or two to show the person's voice.

 Group Discussion

• **Group work:** Ask the children to work in small groups. Each group will discuss how old the house might be, and when they think this photograph may have been taken. They will need to be detectives and look very closely for clues in the picture. Good examples are: old-fashioned door, girl's clothes, dog, house number, curtain. After a few minutes, invite the groups to feed back to the class, through an elected spokesperson

Drama

• **Duologue:** Ask the children to work in pairs. This time, they must act out the scene with one being the child, and the other the dog. Once they are in position, they must deliver one or two lines to show what they are thinking.

• **Group drama:** In small groups, the children pretend they are 'trick or treating' on Halloween. They knock on the door of the house in the picture and see the little girl starting out at them through the letter box. Will they be able to persuade her to come out and join in their spooky fun? Complete the story.

Extension

• **Discussion:** Ask the children to get into groups of about three or four. Their task is to consider the phrase 'a dog is a man's best friend' and to decide if this is true or not. Why do so many of us like dogs? What does a dog provide us with? Why do we actually keep pets? Share feedback in a final plenary.

KNOCK, KNOCK!

Do you know any 'knock, knock' jokes? If you can't remember any make some up and write them on the sheet.

Learn your jokes off by heart and then entertain your friends and family with them.

You might like to perform your jokes with a friend, standing either side of a pretend letter box. Instead of 'knock, knock', why not say 'rattle, rattle'!

_____

_____

_____

_____

_____

_____

_____

_____

_____

_____

_____

TEACHER'S NOTES

Introduction

• Load up the Mind's Eye CD-ROM. You may like to tell the children what the title of the session is before you reveal the image, or just open up the picture and watch their initial reactions to it.

• With the whole image in view, elicit the children's first impressions of the scene. Establish the type of wild cats in the picture. Discuss where in the world this may be. Look carefully at the landscape, ground, skies, horizon. Where do we usually find wild cats like these?

Familiarisation

• Elicit the children's prior knowledge and experience of big cats. Have they seen them before either in captivity or in the wild? Refer to holidays, trips, television programmes, films and books.

• Do the children think this is real? Would these three different big cats really be standing side by side? How else could this image have been created?

Exploration

• Invite the children to think back to 'Disney-type' films they may have seen involving wild animals (e.g. 'Lion King', 'Tarzan', 'Jungle Book'). Explore what it is that we like so much about stories set in the jungle.

• If the image was taken from such a film, why might the three big cats be strolling together? What could the scenario be that would bring these three together in this way? What are they looking at?

Lion (African), jaguar (South American) and tiger (Asian/Indian) on plains landscape (digital composite).
© Renee Lynn/Stone/Getty Images

ACTIVITIES

Speaking

• **Paired role-play:** In pairs, ask the children to imagine they are seated in an open-topped jeep, exploring the plains of Africa together on safari. They must try to convey their excitement or fear at seeing wild animals through their facial expressions and dialogue. Encourage them to react to the sights they see together. One person could be nervous, the other relaxed.

• **Word tennis:** Invite two volunteers to sit opposite one another at the front of the class. One player 'serves' by calling out the name of a jungle animal. The other 'returns' with a new animal. Each player must continue playing until someone hesitates or repeats an animal already called.

Listening

• **Jungle sounds:** What sounds might you hear in the jungle at night? In pairs or small groups, the children create a short presentation in which they simulate the sounds of the jungle at night, with crickets and fireflies, monkeys, birds, big cats and so on. Listen to each piece.

• **Memory game:** Seat the class in a large circle. Take turns reciting the following line and then adding a new animal at the end: *Last summer I went on safari and I saw... .* Before inserting a new animal of their own choosing, each person must try to remember all those that have gone before.

Group Discussion

• **Class debate:** Has anyone seen big cats like these in a zoo or safari park? How do the children feel about keeping animals in captivity? (You may have to explain this word further.) Should all wild animals remain in the wild? What are the benefits of keeping animals in zoos and safari parks? Hold a class debate.

Drama

• **Group drama:** Ask the children to get into groups of about three or four. The children are employees in a zoo that has a big problem: one of the big cats cannot be seen in the enclosure where it should be. Has it escaped? Where could it have gone? The team of staff must solve the case.

Extension

• **Jungle rap:** In pairs or small groups, invite the children to write, rehearse and perform their very own jungle rap. Encourage them to think about the sights and sounds of the jungle. You may want them to give the rap an environmental/conservation feel that warns them to look after the jungle and not to interfere in the lion's kingdom!

Name _____ Date _____

If you were an animal in the jungle, what would you be? There are hundreds of animals to choose from.

Once you have decided, write a short speech giving reasons for your choice. Then read your speech aloud to the rest of the class.

_____

_____

_____

_____

_____

_____

_____

_____

_____

_____

_____

_____

TEACHER'S NOTES

Introduction

- Load up the Mind's Eye CD-ROM. You may like to tell the children what the title of the session is before you reveal the image, or just open up the picture and watch their initial reactions to it.

- With the whole image in view, elicit the children's first impressions of the scene. Where do they think it is? Where have they seen windmills before? Is there a place in this country – or another country altogether – famous for windmills? (Holland)

Familiarisation

- Encourage the children to look more closely at the image and to hunt for other clues to find out where the photograph was taken. Clues are a flat area, sheep and fields (rural), green grass and reeds, temperate climate.

- Elicit the children's prior knowledge of windmills. Establish their function and discuss the words 'wind' and 'mill'. Establish why it was built here particularly, close to a canal (for transportation of goods) and on a flat plain (for wind).

Exploration

- Invite the children to explore, using paper and pencils, what the interior of the windmill looks like. Share designs, too. Encourage the children to consider not only the rooms and facilities inside, but also the inner workings of the windmill and how it might actually work. For a real sketch, visit: www.shipleywindmill.org.uk/sec.htm

- Is the wind blowing now? How can we tell? Invite the children to find clues that could tell us whether the wind is blowing or not (reeds and trees bent over, ripples on the canal).

Windmill in rural Holland.
© Ingram Publishing/Alamy

ACTIVITIES

Speaking

- **Word game:** Ask the children to imagine they are in the location in the picture, on a canal boat. Take it in turns to share words and phrases to describe the journey (e.g. *relaxing, peaceful, boring, birds singing, sunshine beating down, boat chugging*).

- **Explanations:** In pairs, the children must imagine that one person has never seen a windmill before. The other person must explain its features and uses, without ever using their hands (it's harder than you think!).

Listening

- **Chain of sounds:** Explain to the class that they are going to recreate the different sounds of a windmill by dividing up into sections to create each different sound, then putting them all together again. Different parts could include the sound of the wind, sails, wheels, cogs, hoists, grinding machines and grain pouring out. For help and ideas, visit the website referred to above.

Group Discussion

- **Group discussion:** Seat the class in a large circle and initiate a discussion about wind power. What else could it be used for? What sorts of things could it drive? Encourage the children to consider ways in which wind power is used today and new ways in which it could be used in the future.

Drama

- **Group plays:** In groups of about three or four, the children prepare and perform a short role-play in which a group of friends visit an old, disused windmill. The mill was closed down many years before and now houses nothing but rats and birds. The children look around it, and then go to leave, when suddenly the sails start turning. What could be happening?

Extension

- **Presentation:** Ask the children to prepare a short presentation, in pairs or small groups, on windmills. They can use a range of source materials, including websites like the one above, encyclopaedias, CD-ROMs and magazines. (See activity sheet for more details.)

THE WORLD OF WINDMILLS

What have you learned about windmills? What else would you like to know?

Prepare a short talk on windmills to present to the rest of the class.

Begin by making some notes on what you already know about windmills.

_____

_____

_____

_____

_____

_____

Now see if you can find out more windmill facts by using the Internet, books and magazines. Try to find the oldest, tallest, fastest and widest windmills!

_____

_____

_____

_____

_____

TEACHER'S NOTES

Introduction

• Play the first few seconds of the audio clip and then pause it. Invite the children to explain what could be making this sound. Could it be human? Or animal?

• Continue to play the whole clip for the class. Discuss the children's first impressions and establish that it could be the cackle of a witch.

Familiarisation

• Discuss why we often imagine that witches laugh in this way. What are the traditional characteristics of a witch? What do we think of when we hear the word? Elicit the children's first responses and write down some key words on the board.

• Elicit the children's prior knowledge and experience of fictional witches. Where and when have they seen them? List the books, films, shows and events that have witches in them such as 'The Wizard of Oz', 'The Lion, the Witch and the Wardrobe', 'Snow White', Roald Dahl's 'The Witches' or Halloween. Do these witches share similar characteristics?

Exploration

• Encourage the children to consider why this particular witch might be laughing in this way. Is she casting a spell, tricking somebody or stirring a potion?

• Play the clip once again and ask the children to close their eyes and imagine they are with the witch in her lair. Then share words and phrases to describe how they might feel (e.g. *frightened, nervous, collie-wobbles, spine-tingling, teeth chattering*).

Audio clip
WITCH-TYPE CACKLE (03 secs)

ACTIVITIES

Speaking

• **Magic spells:** Working in pairs, invite the children to devise their own magic spells and witches' chants along the lines of 'hocus-pocus' or 'double, double, toil and trouble'. Discuss these examples together; focus on the use of rhyme, repetition, alliteration and syllables to make the spell sound interesting and evil.

• **Talking partners:** Ask the children to work in pairs. Their task is to discuss, and then write down, a character profile of the average witch, describing her appearance, personality, likes and dislikes and any unusual habits. Share the profiles at the end of the session: how similar are they?

Listening

• **Eerie noises:** Discuss with the children the sort of sounds that might accompany a witch's cackle. What other sounds would you hear in a film about witches? (For example: *howling wind, a cat mewing, a scream, a cauldron bubbling.*) In pairs, the children practise putting together eerie sounds that might accompany a witch's cackle. Play the audio clip again and invite each pair to perform their sounds at the same time.

Group Discussion

• **Class discussion:** Who is the most frightening witch the children have come across? Invite the children to share their views on the witches they find most scary and identify what it is that makes them so frightening.

• **Group discussion:** Divide the class into groups of about three. Each group must begin a brief discussion on fairy tales, with a particular focus on the villains or 'baddies' that so many fairy tales seem to feature. Ask the children to consider why so many fairy tales and traditional folk tales have villains in them. Is it so that we can then have a hero? Is it because we like to see good conquering evil?

Drama

• **Group plays:** Ask the children to get into groups of about three or four. Their task is to create a short sketch in which a group of friends encounter the witch in the audio clip. Perhaps they are exploring an old house, or walking in a dark forest. Encourage the children to practise their reactions to the sound of the cackle, which could be played halfway through their drama.

Extension

• **Presentations:** Ask the children to get into small groups (three or four is ideal). Their task is to rehearse and perform a short sketch in which a group of friends hold a Halloween party. Each guest comes dressed in a Halloween costume but they soon realise that there is one more guest than they expected! Which one is the real witch?

Name _____ Date _____

If you were a witch with a bubbling cauldron, what would you put in it to make your evil potion? What would the purpose of your potion be?

Think of some really unusual ingredients to make your own spooky potion. Give it a name and once your recipe is ready, read it out to your friends.

Remember to use your best witch's voice and throw in some good cackling sounds too!

TEACHER'S NOTES

Introduction

• Play the first few seconds of the audio clip and then pause it. Invite the children to guess what is happening in the clip.

• Continue to play the whole clip for the class. Discuss the children's first impressions and establish that the sound is cathedral bells ringing.

Familiarisation

• Replay the clip and then invite the children to identify what else is happening in the scene. What other sounds can be heard that might give them clues as to where this church or cathedral is located? (Traffic can be heard, so it is in a town or city.)

• Play the audio clip once again and see if anyone can identify how many different bells are actually being rung.

Exploration

• Invite the children to share their prior knowledge and experience of church bells. When do they usually ring? What do we think of when we hear them? Good examples are weddings, celebrations, villages, steeples, Sunday Mass.

• Discuss how church bells like these are traditionally rung. Invite three or four children to the front of the class to simulate the pulling and letting go of the bell ropes. Warn them against holding on at the wrong moments, as the bells would be heavier than the bell ringers! Does anyone know what the art of bell ringing is called? (Campanology)

Audio clip
ST PAUL'S (42 secs)

ACTIVITIES

Speaking

• **The big day:** Explore how the children might feel if the bells were ringing to signify a special day. What would the sound mean to them? Could it mean something sad had happened? Share responses in groups/class discussion.

• **Sharing thoughts:** Seat the children in a large circle as a class, or in smaller groups of five or six. Invite them to each imagine they are getting married in a few months. If they could wear any outfit, and travel by any kind of transport to and from the church, what would they choose (and why)?

Listening

• **Bell sounds:** Divide the class into groups of four or five. Ask the groups to simulate the sounds of the bells in the clip using their voices, taking turns around the group. Play the clip a few more times to enable the children to identify different bell pitches and find any recognisable pattern being repeated. The groups practise and then perform their pieces to the class.

Group Discussion

• **Class discussion:** Initiate a class discussion on the difference between churches and cathedrals. What is the purpose of each? What are the children's experiences of cathedrals and churches? How long do they think it might take to build a church or a cathedral? Can they draw each to show the differences?

• **Group discussion:** Why do people attend church? What role does a church or a cathedral play in people's lives? Elicit the children's ideas and experiences of holy buildings. Encourage them to think of the names of buildings from a range of different religions. Is there a common theme that binds them together (collective worship, peace and quiet, community etc.)?

Drama

• **Group drama:** In groups of about four or five, the children act out a mini-play in which a group of friends visit a church or cathedral in the evening when there is no one about. Unexpectedly, the bells begin to ring, when they thought there was no one in the bell tower. Who could it be?

Extension

• Encourage the children, working in small groups or pairs, to begin a mini-project on holy buildings. Invite them to collec pictures of buildings from a range of different faiths, and to write a small paragraph next to each describing its features, uses and general importance within the daily lives of its congregation.

Name _____ Date _____

Listen to the clip of the cathedral bells again. Think about the atmosphere that the bells create in a town or city. Do they make you feel happy or sad? Excited or nervous?

Write a short poem in which you describe the sound of the bells ringing and what this means to you.

Introduction

- Play the first few seconds of the audio clip and then pause it. Invite the children to explain what could be making this sound.

- Continue to play the whole clip for the class. Discuss the children's first impressions and invite them to explain what sort of animal is making this noise (cockerel crowing).

Familiarisation

- What do we think of when we hear this noise? Invite the children's first responses, i.e. *early morning, on a farm, countryside sounds, up at dawn*, etc.

- Elicit the children's prior knowledge and experience of cockerel sounds. Have they ever stayed on a farm and experienced the sounds of the various animals at dawn? What was it like?

Exploration

- Play the audio clip again. Encourage the children to describe the location that is in their minds when they hear this sound. Where is the cockerel situated? Describe the scene for the class.

- Begin a discussion in which you consider other birds that make distinctive noises. Can the children think of other examples? Record them on the board and try to include ducks, chickens, parrots, budgies, songbirds, thrushes and pigeons.

Audio clip
COCKEREL (02 secs)

ACTIVITIES

Speaking

- **Rural sounds:** In a large circle, invite the children to share other animal sounds that they would hear on a farm. There are some obvious ones and some that are not so obvious. Keep a tally on the board and see how many you can get up to.

- **Reported conversations:** The cockerel in the clip is associated with morning. When some people hear its crowing, the first thing they think of is breakfast! In pairs, the children discuss their favourite breakfasts. In a final plenary, invite the children to report their partner's favourite. They must listen carefully!

Listening

- **Memory game:** Seat the class in a large circle. Take turns to recite the following line, adding a new task at the end: *When the cockerel crows the farmer knows he must....* Before inserting a new task of their own choosing, each person must try to remember all those that have gone before it, such as milk the cows, feed the chickens, collect the eggs, shear the sheep, harvest the crops.

Group Discussion

- **Class discussion:** Waking up to a cockerel is usually something only farmers do. But how do the rest of us wake up in the morning? A beeping alarm? A clock radio? Being shouted at? Compare methods of waking up in the class. Record the different answers and take a poll to discover the most common.

- **Group discussion:** Divide the class into small groups. Provide each group with a sheet of A3 paper and a marker pen. The task is to think of as many occupations as they can that involve working with animals, like the farmer's job (e.g. *vet, trainer, RSPCA officer, jockey, fisherman*). Share feedback and see which group has come up with the most jobs.

Drama

- **Group play:** In groups of about three or four, the children prepare a short sketch in which they are helping a farmer for the summer holidays. All is well until one of them leaves a gate open and soon dozens of sheep are roaming free! What will they do? What will the farmer say? Complete the scene as a group.

Extension

- **Poem:** The cockerel in the clip reminds us of early morning in the countryside. Invite the children to picture the sights and sounds of early morning in a favourite place they have visited. Ask the pupils to write a poem in which they describe this place at dawn. Features could include: rolling mist, dewy grass, dawn chorus, sun rising, moon fading, cockerel crowing.

Name ________________________________ Date ________________

I'M LATE!

Do you find getting up in the morning easy or hard?

Write a short conversation between you and an adult at home, in which you really don't want to get up, but the other person is insisting that you will be late for school if you don't! What will you say? Will you ever get out of bed?

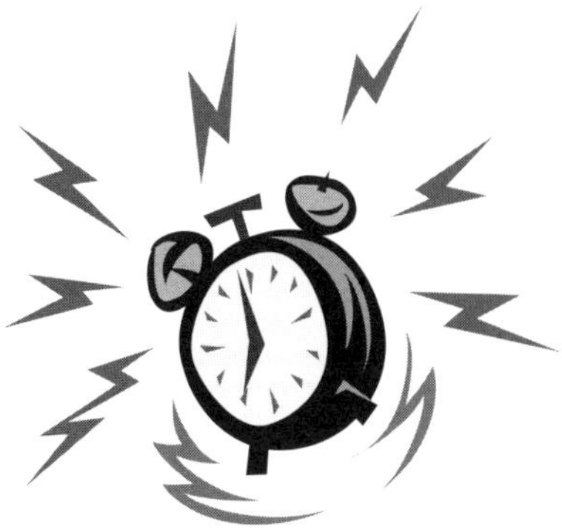

Write a few lines, then learn them off by heart and perform the conversation with a friend.

TEACHER'S NOTES

Introduction

• Play the first few seconds of the audio clip and then pause it. Invite the children to explain what could be making this sound.

• Continue to play the whole clip for the class. Discuss the children's first impressions and establish that it is the sound of footsteps, possibly climbing a stone staircase.

Familiarisation

• Replay the clip and then share ideas about where this person could be walking. Listen carefully to the echoing sound of the footsteps. Does this suggest they are in a tower, like a turret in a castle or a church? Are the footsteps getting closer or further away?

• Elicit the children's prior knowledge and experience of stone staircases. Where have they encountered them before?

Exploration

• Play the audio clip once again. Invite suggestions from the children about who, or what is walking up the stone staircase towards them. Where are they? What might happen next?

• Encourage the children to express how they might feel if they heard these footsteps coming towards them in a strange, dark place like a castle keep. Record key words and phrases such as: *haunted house, ghostly walk, dragging feet over hard stone on the board*.

Audio clip
FOOTSTEPS ON STONE (12 secs)

ACTIVITIES

Speaking

• **Talking pairs:** In pairs, the children share ideas about why they might find themselves in a castle keep, listening to someone approaching. They could be a prisoner awaiting execution or waiting to be released or rescued, a prince or princess banished to the tower, etc.

• **Sharing ideas:** Play the clip once again. Ask the children to imagine that this is the sound of someone climbing a great stone tower. The question is: what can they see from the top? Can the children picture themselves in the scene and then describe the view? The landmarks could include a vast forest, a medieval city, a battleground, an ocean.

Listening

• **Sounds medley:** Can the children sense that there is something ghostly about the footsteps in the clip? What other ghostly sounds can the children make? Invite volunteers to think of, and then share, ghostly sounds (e.g. *creaky door, whistling window, rattling windows, ghostly whispers*).

Group Discussion

• **Class discussion:** Begin a class discussion about how buildings have changed through the ages. Discuss the age of their own homes. What will our homes look like in another 200 years? Will we all be living in skyscrapers with lifts? What do the children think?

Drama

• **Group role-play:** In groups of about three or four, the children act out the following scene set in an old castle. They climb the steps to the top of one of the towers and find a strange room. Suddenly the door closes behind them! They hear the sound of footsteps coming up the stairs. There was no else in the castle when they entered, so who is it? Complete the scene.

• **Duologue:** In pairs, the children role-play a short conversation either side of a cellar door. One person has locked themselves inside the cellar and can't get out! The other person tries to keep them calm and assure them that help will come shortly.

Extension

• **Narrated story:** Begin an improvised story that the children contribute to by adding a line each time, around a circle. You could begin with the line: *The princess sat in the great tower, gazing out of the window and wondering if she would ever be free again...*

BUMPS IN THE NIGHT...

Write a poem to describe how you feel when you hear something go 'bump' in the night. Will you go to investigate the noise, or will you pull the duvet over your head and hide?

Make your poem as exciting as possible for your readers. Your job is to make them feel scared, so use lots of creepy phrases such as creaky floorboards and spooky shadows.

Now learn your poem off by heart and perform it to your teacher or group.

TEACHER'S NOTES

Introduction

- Play the first few seconds of the audio clip and then pause it. Invite the children to suggest what the sound could be.

- Continue to play the whole clip to the class. Discuss the children's first impressions and invite them to suggest where this sound is usually heard (at a racetrack).

Familiarisation

- Elicit the children's prior knowledge and experience of car racing. Try to establish together what type of race this is (Formula One).

- Play the audio clip again and invite the children to guess how fast these cars may be going. How fast does it sound? Can the children identify any cars slowing down for a bend, or is this on a straight road? How many cars can they hear?

Exploration

- Explore the atmosphere of race meetings by brainstorming key words and phrases on a mind-map on the board. You may wish to start the children off with: *exciting, exhilarating, deafening noise, dangerous, thrilling, lightning speeds.*

- What sort of qualities do the children think a racing driver might need? Again, invite them to suggest words and phrases that describe a racing driver's character, such as *calm, quick thinking, strong, well co-ordinated, determined, competitive.* Does anyone think they have what it takes to become a driver themselves?

Audio clip
FORMULA ONE (23 secs)

ACTIVITIES

Speaking

- **Paired work:** In pairs, ask the children to think of as many types of race as they can, and to write them down ready to share with the class at the end. Examples include: *horse, yacht, dog, bicycle, snail* and *three-legged*!

Listening

- **Reporting:** In pairs, the children discuss their knowledge of cars. What are their favourite cars? If they could have any car to race in, which would they choose? Emphasise that both girls and boys often watch races and there are a number of very talented female racing drivers. (Why should boys have all the fun?)

- **Circle race:** Seated in a circle, the children each have a number. Call out two different numbers each time and those children must get up, run around the circle and return to their places; the first one back wins. Try sitting in different shapes to simulate different racetracks.

 Group Discussion

- **Class discussion:** Discuss the idea of speed and why so many of us are interested in races of one kind or another. Have humans always been interested in racing? Can the children think of early forms of transport that might have been used for racing? (Roman chariot racing, early forms of Olympic events.) What kinds of racing will there be in a hundred years time?

- **Class debate:** Is Formula One racing too dangerous? Are the risks involved too great? What do the children think? Are some forms of racing just too dangerous to be allowed? Or is it the danger of it all that makes racing so thrilling for competitors and spectators alike?

Drama

- **Group scene:** Inform the children that they are going to create group scenes in which they play the role of spectators at a Formula One race. Some of the spectators are supporting one race team, while others are supporting a different one. As the race progresses the cars compete and often overtake one another – this will be reflected in the spectators' faces and body language! When the groups are ready, play the audio clip and wait for the cheers (and groans)!

Extension

- **Presentation:** Encourage the children to find out more about racing. They may choose any type of racing (car, boat, horse etc.) and research it using the Internet, CD-ROMs, books and magazines. They may work in pairs, compiling enough information for an oral presentation to the class.

RACING DRIVER WANTED!

In groups of three, rehearse and perform a pretend interview in which one of you plays the part of a potential racing driver and the others are the interviewers.

What sort of person do you want to drive for your team? What sorts of questions should you ask?

Write down some interesting questions and answers. Perform your interview to the rest of the group.

Interviewer 1: _____

_____

Candidate: _____

_____

Interviewer 2: _____

_____

Candidate: _____

_____

Interviewer 1: _____

_____

Candidate: _____

_____

Interviewer 2: _____

_____

Candidate: _____

_____

TEACHER'S NOTES

Introduction

- Play the first few seconds of the audio clip and then pause it. Invite the children to explain what could be making this sound.

- Continue to play the whole clip for the class. Discuss the children's first impressions and establish that it is (or could be) the sound of pots and pans being knocked over.

Familiarisation

- Replay the clip and then discuss how embarrassing it can be when we knock things over or accidentally drop items! Make a list on the board of the items that make the most noise when dropped, such as metal pots and pans, glasses, metal trays, tins, cutlery.

- Share embarrassing stories of times when things have been knocked over by accident.

Exploration

- Play the audio clip once again. Encourage the children to suggest other possible reasons for the noise; what else could it be? Good suggestions are: *a pile of tins in a supermarket, tools in a hardware store, opening an untidy sports cupboard, clowns in a circus.*

- Invite the children to suggest actual scenarios for the sound. Can they imagine themselves near where an accident has just happened? Can they describe what they see?

Audio clip
POTS AND PANS (05 secs)

ACTIVITIES

Speaking

- **Audio captions:** Play the clip again and focus the children's attention on the silence that follows the crashes. What could be put in this silence? What usually follows such an accident? Is it applause, an apology, a shout, laughter? In pairs, the children prepare a short piece of drama that follows on from the clip. Then play the clip and invite each pair to perform their piece as it finishes.

- **Paired conversations:** Ask the children to work in pairs. Their task is to make a list of adjectives that could be used to describe how they might feel if the noise on the clip was caused by them knocking something over. Examples could include: *embarrassed, silly, clumsy, unlucky, ashamed, amused.*

Listening

- **Sounds medley:** Discuss the kinds of words that signify an accident of some sort. These are onomatopoeic words like: *smash, clatter, bang, fizz, wallop.* List these on the board. Then invite the children to put several words together, each one called out by different children in a line, to simulate large-scale mishaps!

Group Discussion

- **Class discussion:** Has anyone ever caused a clumsy accident when the school has been having lunch? How did everyone react? What is the best way to react when you see someone dropping something or knocking something over? Should we laugh, applaud, shout, or sympathise and help them to make amends? Does it depend on whether or not the culprit is embarrassed?

- **Group discussion:** In small groups or pairs, invite the children to come up with a 'survival guide' to coping with embarrassment. They will need to think first about how being embarrassed can affect us (red-faced, sweating, shortness of breath, panicking, upset) and then think of ways of beating these symptoms (deep breathing, laughing it off, remembering other people can be clumsy too).

Drama

- **Group sounds:** The sounds on the clip are entitled 'Pots and pans falling over'. But what other sounds could be recreated to suggest an accident of some kind? Encourage the children to work in pairs or small groups, devising comical sounds to signify another accident. Good ones to try are: skidding of brakes and a crunch; falling object (whistling) and a bang.

Extension

- **Group plays:** Ask the children to get into small groups (three or four is ideal). Each group must create their own short sketch in which someone accidentally knocks something over in a very public place. Venues could include a supermarket, library, art gallery or musical instrument shop! One person will be the accident-prone character and the others will need to react in an appropriate manner. Share performances at the end of the session.

WHOOPS-A-DAISY!

Imagine your friend has accidentally broken one of your favourite toys. How would you react? What would you say?

Write a short conversation that you might have with your friend about the mishap. Will you forgive them or argue?

Remember: accidents are never done on purpose – that's why they are called accidents!

_____

_____

_____

_____

_____

_____

_____

_____

_____

_____

_____

Now learn the words and perform them as a mini-play with a friend.

TEACHER'S NOTES

Introduction

- Play the first few seconds of the audio clip and then pause it. Invite the children to explain what could be making this sound.

- Continue to play the whole clip for the class. Discuss the children's first impressions and invite them to suggest what sort of animal could be making this noise. You may wish to record the possibilities on the board.

Familiarisation

- Replay the clip once again and then explain that the grunts are actually coming from a rhinoceros! Elicit children's impressions again – did they expect a rhino to sound like this? What were they expecting the animal to be?

- Share the children's prior knowledge and experience of rhinos. Where have they seen them before? What do they know about them? Has anyone heard one before?

Exploration

- Play the clip once again and discuss what the rhino might be 'saying' here. Could it be a distress signal, or a battle cry, or something else?

- Invite the children to suggest theories about what is happening in the clip to make the rhino make this noise. The children can describe the scene, explaining who or what could be disturbing the rhino. They can be as imaginative as they wish!

Audio clip
RHINOCEROS (20 secs)

ACTIVITIES

Speaking

- **Animal noises:** Seat the children in a circle. Introduce the idea of 'scary animal' noises. Which animals do we find scary and what sorts of noises are traditionally thought of as frightening (i.e. *roar, growl, screech, howl, hiss*)? Record these words on the board. Invite volunteers to make the different sounds.

- **Paired conversations:** Ask the children to work in pairs. Their task is to compile a list of adjectives that may be used to describe a rhinoceros. Encourage them to try to capture not only appearance, but also the way the rhino moves and perhaps even thinks. Good words are: *sturdy, solid, tough, stubborn.*

Listening

- **Reporters:** Explain to the class that most people, if left alone with a rhino, would feel frightened. However, some people cannot bear to be left alone with a spider as they suffer from a phobia. In pairs, ask the children to share their phobias about animals and insects. At the end, ask them to report their partners' phobias to the group.

Group Discussion

- **Class discussion:** Begin a further discussion on rhinos, building on the initial talk in the 'Familiarisation' above. Present the children with some interesting facts or check out the website: www.rhinos-irf.org. Rhinos have been on Earth for 50 million years. Some rhinos were woolly, stood six feet tall at the shoulders and weighed 3 tonnes. Introduce and discuss the word 'extinction'.

- **Class debate:** Should rhinos be kept in zoos? What would happen if they were all sent back to the wild? Do zoos and safari parks help to protect animals from extinction, or do they take away their freedom?

Drama

- **Group drama:** Divide the class into small groups. Play the audio clip once again, during which the children must close their eyes and imagine they are on a safari holiday where rhinos are found in the wild. Their jeep is confronted by a giant rhino. What happens next? Invite the groups to rehearse and perform a sketch on this theme.

Extension

- **Presentation:** Encourage the children to conduct their own research into rhinos, using websites (including the one above), CD-ROMs, books and magazines. Ask them to compile some fascinating 'rhino facts' that can be presented to the class in a plenary session.

Name _____ Date _____

DO YOU SEE WHAT I SEE?

Find a partner to work with. Imagine you are out shopping when suddenly you hear a strange grunt and turn around to see a rhino, which has escaped from the zoo. What will you say? What will you do?

Write down some words to say to each other and then perform your conversation to the class.

_____

_____

_____

_____

_____

_____

_____

_____

_____

_____

_____

_____

TEACHER'S NOTES

Introduction

- Play the first few seconds of the audio clip and then pause it. Invite the children to suggest what the sound could be.

- Continue to play the whole clip for the class. Discuss the children's first impressions and establish that this is a tennis match in progress. Discuss the familiar sounds of the tennis ball hitting the strings of the racket and the pauses in between.

Familiarisation

- Elicit the children's prior knowledge and experience of tennis matches. What are the names of the most famous tournaments (Queens, Davis Cup, Wimbledon)? Has anyone ever visited one of them?

- Play the audio clip again and see if you can establish the location of this match. Encourage the children to listen out for traffic to see if this is in a town, such as Wimbledon, or the countryside.

Exploration

- Invite the children to close their eyes and imagine they are at Wimbledon, watching the final on Centre Court. Can they describe the atmosphere? Record words and phrases on a mind-map on the board (*hear a pin drop, nervous excitement, great occasion, Mexican waves*).

- Some tennis matches can be quite a battle between two 'gladiators'. Can the children think of other such battles between two sporting competitors? List the possibilities on the board.

Audio clip
TENNIS (13 secs)

ACTIVITIES

Speaking

- **Word tennis:** Ask for two volunteers to sit opposite one another at the front of the class. One player 'serves' by calling out the name of a sport. The other 'returns' with a different one, and so on, until one person hesitates or repeats a sport already mentioned.

- **Talking pairs:** Divide the class into pairs. Each pair must discuss the qualities needed to become a great athlete or sportsperson. The children can write these attributes down and present them to the class at the end. You may wish to start them off with: *stamina, fitness, dedication, self-discipline, talent.*

Listening

- **Commentating:** Divide the class into groups of three. Two group members are playing a sport together. In the first scene, the players pretend to play and the commentator gives a commentary on what is happening. In the second scene, the commentator leads and the players must act out the commentary, putting actions to what is said!

Group Discussion

- **Class discussion:** Initiate a discussion into why so many of us are fascinated by sport. Why do we like to watch and play sport so much? Invite the children to consider what it is about sport that appeals to us. What is the purpose of sport? What would life be like without any form of competitive games?

 Drama

- **Duologues:** In pairs, the children act out a scene in which one person has just come off a tennis court having lost a really important match. The other is a friend who tries to console the player, cheering them up and trying to build up their confidence again.

- **Group plays:** In groups of five, the children act out a scene where two tennis players are playing a match. There is an umpire and there are two ball boys/girls waiting by the side of the net. The ball boys/girls are making faces at each other from across the court. One of the players notices this and complains to the umpire. What happens next?

Extension

- **Presentation:** Ask the children to conduct some research using the Internet, CD-ROMs, books or magazines on their own favourite sport. In pairs or individually, the children prepare a short talk for the class, sharing some interesting facts about their chosen sport and explaining why they enjoy watching or playing it.

Name _____ Date _____

TAKE UP TENNIS!

Imagine you are helping to organise a tennis tournament.
Write and perform a short radio advertisement to
persuade listeners to buy tickets for the event.

You may want to include:

- names of famous tennis players who are competing
- times and dates of matches
- refreshments and facilities
- ticket prices.

Make your advert short, snappy and catchy!

_____

_____

_____

_____

_____

_____

_____

_____

_____

_____

_____

TEACHER'S NOTES

Introduction

• Play the first few seconds of the audio clip and then pause it. Invite the children to explain what they think the sound is.

• Continue to play the whole clip for the class. Discuss the children's first impressions and establish that it is the sound of a thunderstorm in full swing.

Familiarisation

• Replay the clip and then invite the children to share their own experiences of thunder. Does it really sound like this?

• Initiate a discussion about how thunder is created. What produces the sound of thunder? When do we usually hear thunder? What follows thunder (rainstorm)? How can you tell when a storm is getting closer? Who is the Viking God of thunder (Thor)?

Exploration

• How do we feel when we hear thunder like this? Encourage the children to share their responses, expressing their ideas in words and short phrases that are associated with thunder, for example: *scary, deafening, uncomfortable, menacing, angry monster, roaring, grumbling*.

• Explore the dramatic impact that thunder and lightning can bring to a story setting. How, and why, does thunder make stories more dramatic? Does the idea of it scare readers and build tension? What sort of characters do we expect to find in a story set in a thunderstorm? (People who are lost, witches, vampires, werewolves.)

Audio clip
RUMBLY THUNDER (03 secs)

ACTIVITIES

 ### Speaking

• **Story narrating:** In a large circle, the children narrate an improvised story that begins: *On a dark and stormy night...* Each child contributes one line each time. Encourage the children to try to use lots of description, referring to the moody atmosphere created by the storm.

• **Paired conversations:** Ask each pair to imagine they are two friends caught up in a storm at night. They are in a forest, when suddenly lightning flashes and the distant sound of thunder tells them a storm is approaching. How do they feel? Where will they go? Does the forest seem more frightening in a storm?

 ### Listening

• **Eerie sounds:** What else might we expect to hear if we were caught up in the dark and stormy night described in the story above? Ask the children to get into groups of about three and to explore different spooky sounds that might go well with the audio clip, such as: *wolf howling, owl tooting, wind, footsteps running*. When each group is ready, play back the clip and let the sounds begin!

 ### Group Discussion

• **Weather talk:** Begin a group or class discussion about extreme weather around the world. What sorts of extreme weather conditions have the children heard of? Where do they occur? Has anyone been caught up in a hurricane or a monsoon? How must it feel to be at the mercy of nature in this way?

 ### Drama

• **Group drama:** In groups of about four or five, the children act out a mini-play in which a group of friends are at sea in a small yacht. They see dark clouds assembling in the distance and soon find themselves being tossed about in the middle of a mighty thunderstorm. Will the boat survive the lashing from the waves and the pelting from the driving rain? Finish the scene.

Extension

• **Presentation:** Ask the children, in pairs or small groups, to prepare a short oral presentation to give to the class on the subject of extreme weather. Give each pairing a particular type of climatic event to research, such as *gale, thunderstorm, hurricane, monsoon, drought, ice-cap melting, tsunami*.

Name _____   Date _____

'THUNDERBOLT SKATEBOARDS'

You are making a television advert to sell Thunderbolt Skateboards. The advert will begin with the sound of thunder crashing and show skateboarders in flight.

Write the script for this advertisement and then perform it with your friends. Tell your audience about:

- the amazing tricks you can do on a Thunderbolt skateboard
- the cool colours and amazing designs on the boards
- the price
- where you can buy them.

_____

_____

_____

_____

_____

_____

_____

_____

_____

_____

_____

TEACHER'S NOTES

Introduction

- Play the first few seconds of the audio clip and then pause it. Invite the children to suggest what could be making this sound.

- Continue to play the whole clip for the class. Discuss the children's first impressions and invite them to say what sort of animal could be making this noise. You may wish to record the suggestions on the board.

Familiarisation

- Replay the clip once again and then explain that it is the sound of a whale. Encourage the children to share their impressions of the sound – how does it make them feel? Record key words such as *dreamy, floating, sleepy* and *curious* on the board.

- Elicit the children's prior knowledge and experience of whales. Where have they encountered them? On documentaries, films, museums, in the flesh? How would they feel if they were close to a whale?

Exploration

- What do the children think the whale could be saying? Can we interpret its thoughts and feelings from the changing tones of its call?

- Ask the children to imagine that this sound appears in a fantasy film about a magical world. What could be making the sound now? What sort of atmosphere is created by the sound? Share words and phrases such as *mysterious, dreamy, supernatural, fantastical*.

Audio clip
WHALE SONG (10 secs)

ACTIVITIES

Speaking

- **Coded calls:** The whale is communicating in a way that we cannot understand, almost like a code. Can the children think of their own coded way of speaking to one another? Working in pairs, invite the children to devise a short coded message that only they can understand.

- **Brainstorm:** As a class, consider the world in which whales live. Can the children describe this fascinating place, using their senses? Ask them to suggest words and phrases to describe how the deep ocean might look/sound/feel. Record these words on a mind-map.

Listening

- **Memory game:** Seated in a circle, the children take turns to say the following line: *I went diving in the deep blue sea and I saw...* . The children must add an animal or item that they might encounter when diving. The next person recites the line and all the previous animals, before adding one of their own. They will need to listen carefully!

Group Discussion

- **Class discussion:** Begin a further discussion on whales, building on the initial talk in the 'Familiarisation' above. Present the children with interesting facts. See the websites: www.cetacea.org/whales.htm and www.companyofwhales.co.uk (there are many more). Introduce information about the threats that whales face today (to be investigated by the children in the 'Extension' task below).

Drama

- **Paired drama:** Ask the pupils to work in pairs. The aim is to try to simulate two whales in conversation! Play the audio clip several times to enable the children to grasp the intonation and patterns of the whale song. After practising their pieces, invite volunteers to share them with the class.

- **Group drama:** Ask the children to work in groups of three or four. Each group must enact a short role-play in which they are on a boating holiday. They are having fun in a small yacht when they feel a thump below the hull – it is a giant whale! Though whales are peaceful creatures, it gives everyone a fright!

⏻ Extension

- **Presentation:** Encourage the children to conduct their own research into whales, using websites (including the ones above), CD-ROMs, books ('The Whale's Song' by Dylan Sheldon) and magazines. Ask them to compile some fascinating facts about whales and then share them with the class in a short presentation.

Name _____ Date _____

SAVE OUR WHALES!

Did you know that whales are in danger?
Can you find out why?

Use the Internet, CD-ROMs, books and magazines to
find out about the threats that whales face every day
and use this information to prepare a radio
advertisement for a charity called SAVE OUR WHALES.
You must persuade viewers to give money to the
charity so that they can help the whales to survive.

_____

_____

_____

_____

_____

_____

_____

_____

_____

_____

OPPORTUNITIES FOR CROSS-CURRICULAR LINKS TO QCA SCHEMES OF WORK (DfES Standards Site) in Mind's Eye Y3

Mind's Eye Y3 Unit IMAGES 1-20	Cross-curricular links (QCA Schemes of work)
CAVE CARVINGS	**Geography:** Unit 5 Where in the world is Barnaby Bear?; **Science:** Unit 3D Rocks and soils; **ICT:** Units 3A Combining text and graphics; **Art and design:** Unit 1C What is sculpture?; Unit 2B Mother Nature
FACE AT THE WINDOW	**Citizenship:** Unit 02 Choices; **Geography:** Unit 19 How and where do we spend our time?
FIRE!	**Science:** Unit 3C Characteristics of materials; **Citizenship:** Unit 04 People who help us
KNIGHTS	**History:** Unit 6B Why have people invaded
MAP READING	**Geography:** Unit 1 Around our school; Unit 18 Connecting ourselves to the world; **PE:** Unit 20 Outdoor and adventurous activities
MAGICAL MARKET	**RE:** Units 1C and 2C Celebrations; **Geography:** Unit 5 Where in the world is Barnaby Bear?
MAZE	**Art and design:** Unit 3B Investigating pattern; **Citizenship:** Unit 01 Taking part – working together
PAINTED FACES	**Geography:** Unit 18 Connecting ourselves to the world; **Citizenship:** Unit 05 Living in a diverse world
PILOTS	**History:** Unit 17 What are we remembering; **Science:** Unit 2E Forces and movement
RIDING HIGH	**Citizenship:** Unit 02 Choices; **Design and technology:** Unit 2A Vehicles
SMUGGLER'S COVE	**Geography:** Unit 4 Going to the seaside; Unit 23 Investigating coasts; **History:** Unit 3 Seaside holidays in the past
SOLDIERS	**Citizenship:** Unit 01 Taking part; Unit 4 People who help us
SPOOKY HOUSE	**History:** Unit 1 What were homes like a long time ago? **Art and design:** Unit 6C A sense of place
STONEHENGE	**Geography:** Unit 9 Village settlers; **History:** Unit 6B Why people invaded and settled in Britain in the past; Unit 18 What was it like to live here in the past? **ICT:** Unit 2C Finding information
UFO	**Geography:** Unit 16 What's in the news?; **Citizenship:** Unit 11 In the media – what's the news? **Design and technology:** Unit 2A Vehicles
UNDERGROUND	**Geography:** Unit 4 Going to the seaside; **Science:** Unit 3D Rocks and soils
UP, UP AND AWAY	**ICT:** Unit 2C Finding information; **Science:** Unit 5C Gases around us; Unit 6E: Forces in action
WHO'S THERE?	**Citizenship:** Unit 03 Animals and us; Unit 09 Respect for property
WILD ANIMALS	**Science:** Unit 6A Interdependence and adaptation; **Citizenship:** Unit 03 Animals and us
WINDMILLS	**Science:** Unit 1E Pushes and pulls; Unit 2E Forces and movement; **ICT:** Unit 2C Finding information

Mind's Eye Y3 Unit SOUNDS 1-10	Cross-curricular links (QCA Schemes of work)
CACKLING WITCH	**Citizenship:** Unit 01 Taking part
CHURCH BELLS	**RE:** Unit 1F What can we learn from visiting a church?; Unit 2D Visiting a place of worship; **Citizenship:** Unit 02 Choices; **Music:** Unit 2 Sounds interesting; Unit 16 Cyclic patterns – exploring rhythms and pulse
COCKEREL	**Citizenship:** Unit 02 Choices; Unit 03 Animals and us
FOOTSTEPS	**History:** Unit 2 What were homes like a long time ago?; **Science:** Unit 1F Sound and hearing
FORMULA ONE	**Science:** Unit 2E Forces and movement; **History:** Unit 13 How has life in Britain changed since 1948?
POTS AND PANS	**Citizenship:** Unit 02 Choices; Unit 09 Respect for property
RHINOCEROS	**Science:** Unit 4B Habitats; **ICT:** Unit 2C Finding information; **Citizenship:** Unit 03 Animals and us
TENNIS	**Science:** Unit 5A Keeping healthy; **PE:** Unit 4 Games activities (2); **ICT:** Unit 2C Finding information; Unit 6A Multimedia presentation
THUNDER	**Geography:** Unit 7 Weather around the world; **ICT:** Unit 2C Finding information; **Science:** Unit 4F Circuits and conductors
WHALE SONG	**Science:** Unit 4B Habitats; **Citizenship:** Unit 03 Animals and us; **ICT:** Unit 2C Finding information; Unit 6D Using the Internet to search large databases and interpret information; **Music:** Unit 9 Animal magic